AN ILLUSTRATED GUIDE TO

HERBS

their medicine and magic

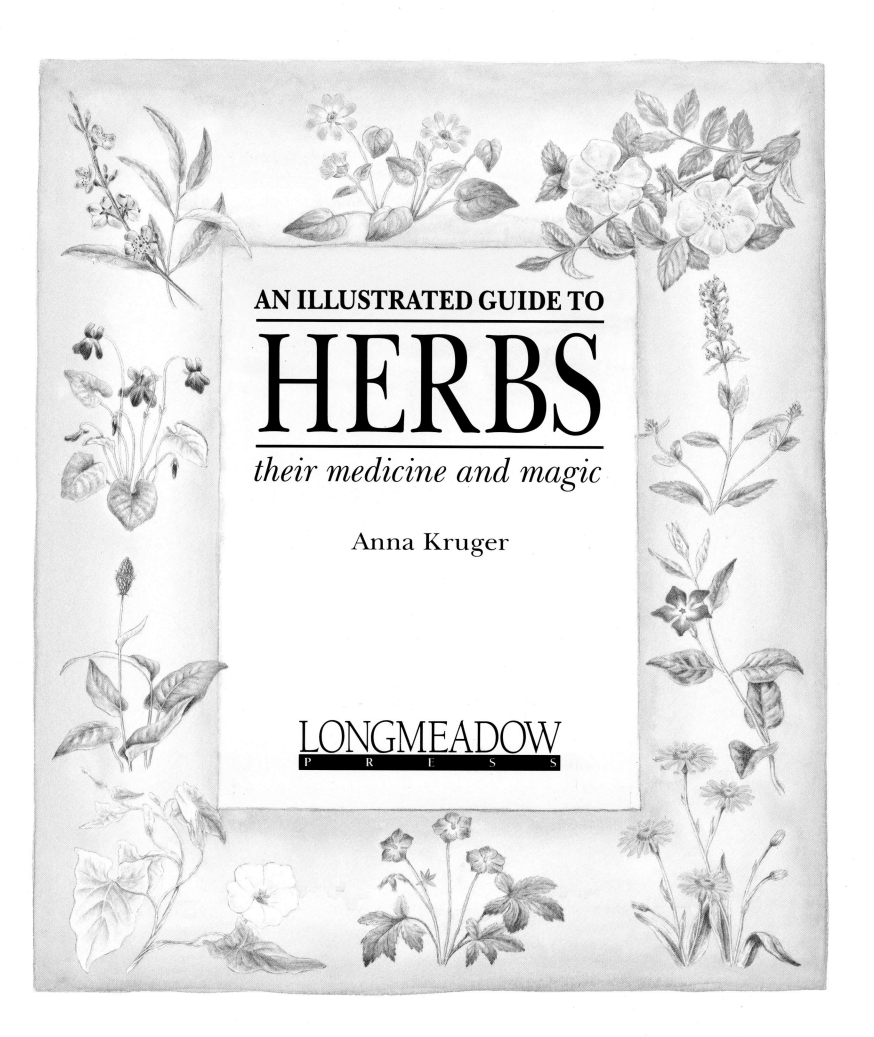

AN ILLUSTRATED GUIDE TO
HERBS
their medicine and magic

Anna Kruger

LONGMEADOW
PRESS

Acknowledgements

The author would like to extend very special thanks to Vera
Wilson, and also acknowledge Maud Grieve's *A Modern Herbal*
(Penguin, 1980, first published 1931), which was an
invaluable source of information in the preparation of this book.

Published by Longmeadow Press, 202 High Ridge Road,
Stamford CT 06904.

Editors: Diana Steedman and ELizabeth Radford
Designers: Anne Doolan and Frances de Rees
Editorial Director: Pippa Rubinstein

ISBN: 0-681-45380-X

Printed in Italy

First Longmeadow Press Edition

0 9 8 7 6 5 4 3 2 1

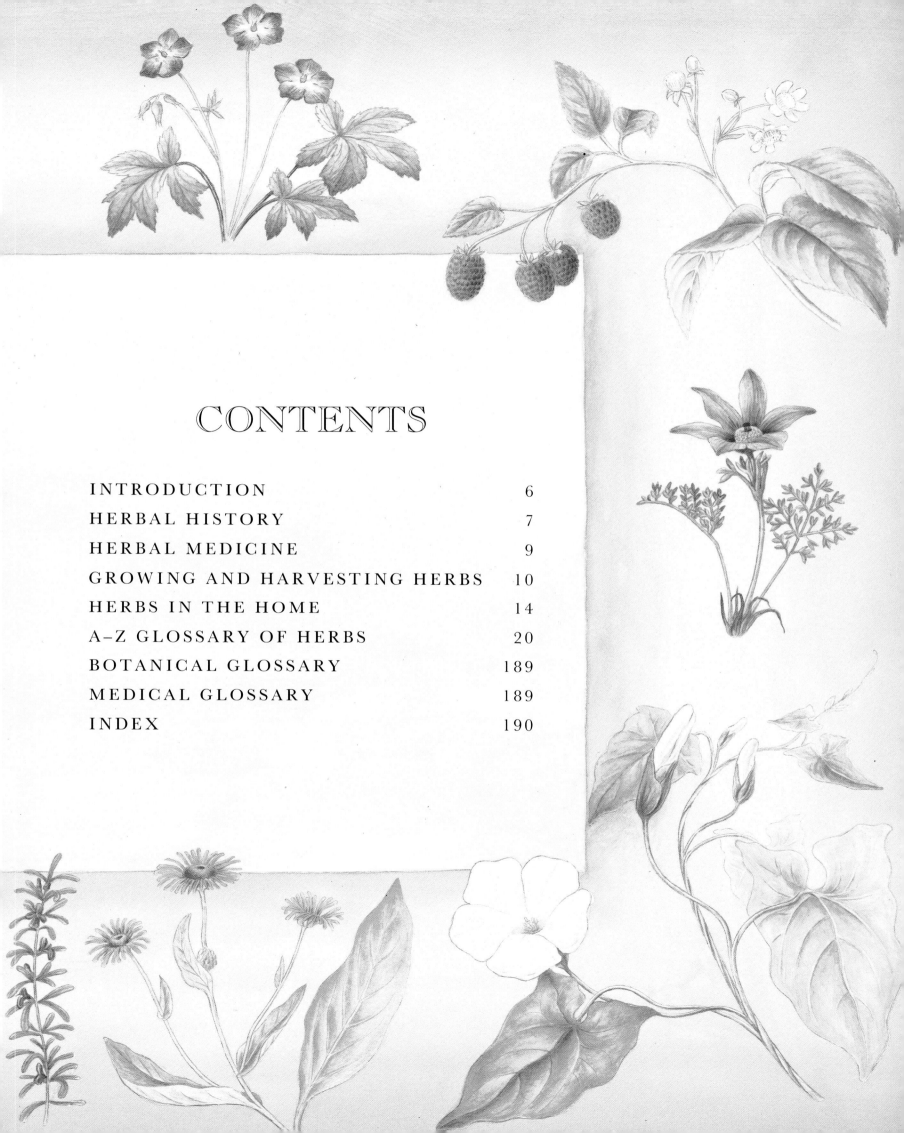

CONTENTS

INTRODUCTION

Herbs are remarkable plants, with a rich and fascinating history that dates back thousands of years. The first official records of medicinal plants, set down on papyrus scrolls and parchments, bear witness to our ancestors' brave experimentation with herbs that might either kill or cure. Despite such occupational hazards, generations of practising herbalists built up an admirable corpus of herbal knowledge. In the monasteries of medieval Europe this accumulated learning of the ancient world was preserved in beautifully illuminated manuscripts by monks, who, naturally, soothed their strained eyes with infusions of rue.

The unofficial history of herbalism was handed down over generations by word of mouth, especially in rural areas where herbs were indispensable, not only for curing ailments, but also for such household tasks as preserving food, dyeing cloth, and repelling fleas. Our ancestors were deeply respectful of herbs: myths and legends sprang up around them, and those who practised the green magic of plants were held in great esteem. Today, we may disparage such notions as superstition, yet we have lost the purely instinctual feel for plants that came so naturally to our forebears. *Herbs, their Medicine and Magic*, is a journey through the fascinating world of herbs, and a tribute to the traditional wisdom of our grandmothers, and the generations of wise women before them.

HERBAL HISTORY

Although the origins of herbalism are uncertain, we do know that the oldest recorded usage of plants was medicinal. In ancient times, people had a close, instinctive relationship with the natural world and depended on it for medicine as well as food. By a lengthy and somewhat dangerous process of trial and error, our ancestors accumulated a wealth of practical knowledge about herbs. Country people were free to collect wild food and they learned ways of using herbs to preserve food and drink for winter consumption. Traditional plant lore was passed down through generations, and indeed was necessary for the survival of many rural communities. Herbs were essential for treating illness since medical attention was either beyond the means of most families or simply non-existent.

Records surviving from ancient Egyptian and Sumerian civilizations dating from before 2500 BC, show how well-acquainted these races were with the medicinal properties of herbs. The famous *Ebers Papyrus*, discovered in 1874, lists over 800 medicinal plants that were commonly prescribed by 1800 BC for illness as well as for ritual and embalming purposes. A parallel development in herbal medicine took place in China and India: herbal preparations are documented in a Chinese pharmacopeia reputed to have been written around 2700 BC, while the *Rig Veda*, one of the ancient Hindu scriptures, lists over 1000 medicinal plants. From Egypt and Mesopotamia herbal knowledge spread to Greece and was soon absorbed into Roman culture. Many legends grew up around Asclepius, the famous Egyptian-born Greek herbalist and teacher who practised as a healer sometime after 1250 BC, aided by his daughters Hygeia and Panacea. Herbalism became closely linked with magic, and many of the prescribed herbs were furnished by itinerant and illiterate root-gatherers who performed special and secret rituals and incantations. With the appearance of Hippocrates (460–377 BC), came the establishment of a scientific system of medicine based on diagnosis and treatment with plant remedies, a system that dispensed with the notion of disease as a visitation from the gods.

The first century AD saw the earliest genuine herbal, *De Materia Medica*, the work of the Greek army doctor Dioscorides. Building on the work of Hippocrates, Dioscorides' herbal described the appearance and properties of over 500 plants, and served as a reference work for the next 150 years. In the same period, the Roman naturalist Pliny produced a lengthy *Natural History* that described plants and their medicinal uses. For the next seven centuries, known collectively as the Dark Ages, the task of keeping alive official herbal knowledge fell to the monasteries where monks copied out texts, practised healing, and tended flourishing herb gardens. Popular reliance on folk remedies, with their successful formula of medicine mixed with magic, continued unabated. During the seventh and eighth centuries the Greek and Roman herbals were translated by Arabic physicians, and they added their own teachings and those acquired via their trading contacts with the East. Avicenna, who was the most celebrated Moslem physician of the time, wrote the *Canon of Medicine*, a classic compilation of medicinal plants, diseases and treatments, which remained a standard reference work until 1650. The tenth century also saw the appearance of the first Anglo-Saxon herbal, the *Leech Book of Bald*, written in the common tongue and with an emphasis on the ritual and the magical.

In the twelfth century, Arabic herbals were translated back into Latin but no new developments took place until some 200 years later when Marco Polo and other Italian explorers opened up trade links with China and India. Venice was established as the centre of the European spice trade and grew exceedingly prosperous since spices were invaluable for preserving and improving the taste of food. The lucrative spice market motivated Portuguese explorers to open up a direct sea route to the East, while the discovery of the New World led to the appearance of new plants and herbal medicines. When the printing press was invented in the fifteenth century, herbals were among the first and most popular books to be published and widely circulated. The Elizabethan age was a great era for herbals and facsimile editions of the most celebrated texts are still widely read for study and for pleasure.

HERBALS AND HERBALISTS

The German *Kreuterbuch* of Tragus, published in 1539, offered more accurate descriptions of herbs, while Turner's *New Herball* offered one of the first scientific botanical studies. A Flemish herbal by Dodoens described the properties of herbs and attempted a classification, and it was this volume, translated into both French and English, that formed the basis of one of the most famous of all herbals, Gerard's *Herball*, published in 1597.

John Gerard (1545–1612)
Gerard was a celebrated surgeon, botanist, and skilled horticulturalist who grew over a thousand common and rare plants in his garden in London's Fetter Lane. His interest in plants prompted gifts of seeds from all over the world. Gerard rearranged and enlarged a Latin version of Dodoens' herbal, by the inclusion of his own experiences, theories and remedies. This herbal became enormously popular, especially when the revised version was brought out by Thomas Johnson in 1633.

ABOVE LEFT: **Virginia Snakeroot**

RIGHT: **The mandrake root was often pictured in human form** (*Ortus Sanitatis, 1497*)

John Parkinson (1567–1650)

A skilled gardener, herbalist and apothecary, Parkinson had a magnificent garden in the Covent Garden district of London. He published two books, *Paradisi in Sole Paradisus Terrestris* and the *Theatricum Botanicum*. The latter ranked among the great herbals of the time.

Nicholas Culpeper (1616–1654)

Culpeper was a herbalist of the people whose remedies were especially popular with the poor inhabitants of London's East End. An iconoclast and centre of controversy throughout most of his life, Culpeper infuriated the medical establishment by translating the *London Pharmacopeia* from Latin to English. His desire was to break the stranglehold of the Royal College of Physicians and restore medicine to those who actually practised and prescribed it, the apothecaries. He subscribed to the theory of astrological botany, believing that the planetary rulership of plants helped to determine their medical application, and was a firm exponent of the Doctrine of Signatures.

The Doctrine of Signatures

This theory proposed that the shape, colour and general appearance of a plant indicated its medicinal application. The theory's main proponent was the sixteenth-century Swiss physician, herbalist and alchemist, Paracelsus, whose belief in the

Nicholas Culpeper – the people's herbalist

active healing principles present in plants anticipated the findings of nineteenth-century chemistry. Culpeper's writing demonstrates a firm adherence to this doctrine, as does the work of William Coles who explained away the absence of God-given signatures in other plants as a sign that man must discover their properties unaided.

THE NEW WORLD

Pilgrims from England and colonists from Europe carried seeds from their native herbs to America and established flourishing herb gardens. At the same time, they learned about the folk medicine of the indigenous peoples and acquired a wide knowledge of medicinal herbs that eventually found its way into Nicholas Monardes' sixteenth-century text *Joyfull Newes out of the Newe Founde Worlde* and Woods' *New England Prospect*. American plants aroused a great deal of interest among botanists who travelled to the New World with plants from their own countries.

DECLINE AND RESURGENCE

In early eighteenth-century Europe, Linnaeus' pioneering work on the classification of plants heralded the division between herbalists and botanists. Plants of all types, not only medicinal plants, were eagerly sought, classified and studied, and the Flora soon replaced the Herbal. Concurrently, advances in chemistry and biochemistry resulted in the isolation and the eventual synthesis of the active principles of plants. With the rise of the pharmaceutical industry, plant-based medicines, flavourings, cosmetics, household cleaners and dyes were replaced by synthetics. Today there is a revival of interest in gentler, plant-based products and remedies, due in part to a dissatisfaction with harsh, petrochemical-based drugs, cosmetics and cleaners and the resultant pollution they cause. With the current awareness of ecological issues and the reaction against synthetic chemical ingredients, plants symbolize and provide a comforting link with the natural world, both present and past.

The Doctrine of Signatures: Flowers with 'eyes' were believed to enhance vision

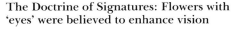

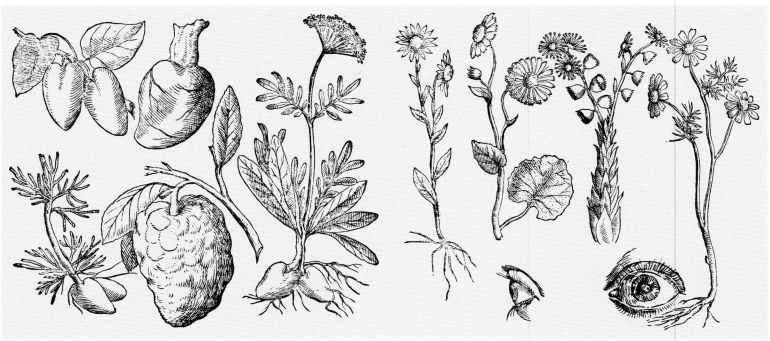

HERBAL MEDICINE

The oldest recorded usage of herbs is medicinal. Today, many Third World countries are very dependent on plant-based remedies, while herbs have provided western medicine with the active ingredients of some of its most important drugs. From the common foxglove (*Digitalis purpurea* and spp.) are derived the heart drugs digoxin and digitoxin; the South American arrow poison, curare, is employed during surgery as a muscle relaxant; cinchona bark (*Cinchona officinalis*) from the Andes is the natural source of quinine, used to treat malaria; and from the opium poppy (*Papaver somniferum*) are extracted the valuable pain killers, morphine and codeine. The tropical rainforests are home to an estimated 50 per cent of the world's plant and animal species, yet, with the accelerating destruction of rainforest habitats, every day up to 50 species are becoming extinct. Rainforest plants are particularly valuable since they are the source of one in four medicines available from pharmacies. Medications for such conditions as malaria, amoebic dysentery, glaucoma, epilepsy and hypertension are derived from rainforest plants, while of the 3000 plants with anti-cancer properties identified by the US National Cancer Institute, 70 per cent originate in rainforests. According to current estimates, 40 million acres of rainforest are disappearing every year, and yet a mere 1 per cent of the plants that flourish in them have been analysed for their medicinal potential. Biochemists investigating the healing possibilities of plants have discovered anti-viral compounds in the Australian Moreton Bay chestnut (*Castanospermum australe*) and research into the possible use of these compounds in the treatment of AIDS is being carried out.

Herbs have complex chemical structures composed of cells and materials such as starches, sugars, proteins, enzymes and fats. Their medicinal effect on humans is due to the active principles or secondary plant products that plants also make but whose function within the plant is not completely understood. The main groups of active principles are known as alkaloids, glycosides, saponins, essential oils, mucilages, tannins and bitters. Morphine, for instance, is a well-known alkaloid and glycosides include those active principles in foxglove, known as cardio-active glycosides, that have a powerful effect on the heart.

Isolating the active principles and synthesizing them into drugs is, however, one of the principal ways in which orthodox medicine differs from medical herbalism. Herbalists prefer to use the whole herb, or medicinal part, not the extract. Originally a single herb, known as a 'simple', was prescribed, and some herbalists may still consider this method particularly effective. Mixtures of herbs are now common and reflect the modern herbalist's knowledge of the workings of the body's systems. Herbalists consider the active principles of plants are safer if the plant or part of the plant is left whole, rather than reduced to the form of a purified extract, since the fresh or dried plant can also contain additional substances that have a balancing effect on the human body. Ephedrine, for example, an alkaloid found in the Chinese herb *Ma Huang* (*Ephedra sinica*), was found to cause a dangerous rise in blood pressure when isolated and taken in drug form for asthma. The whole plant, still used in traditional Chinese medicine, does, however, contain another active ingredient that slows down both heart rate and blood pressure. The balancing or normalizing effect of herbs is particularly clear in those like ginseng (*Panax ginseng*), that are known as adaptogens. These plants affect the body only if the system is under stress or has been damaged in some way; they have no effect on healthy systems. Here we see the other most important difference between orthodox medicine and herbalism. Herbalists treat people in a holistic way that takes into account temperament, diet and lifestyle, not just the relief of symptoms. Disease is seen as a disruption of the system as a whole and treatment to activate the body's self-healing mechanism is considered gentler and less intrusive than the symptomatic relief offered by drugs, as well as being more effective in the long term. Herbal remedies, however, can take much longer to produce effects since they may be treating imbalances in the body that have built up over many years.

Using herbs to treat minor or common ailments is safe, especially if you restrict yourself to those ailments that you would normally treat with proprietary medicines available over the counter. Poisonous herbs, such as aconite (*Aconitum napellus*) are generally not available to the non-professional, but you may still come across powerful and potentially toxic herbs in the wild, such as foxglove. Use only those herbs that you have positively identified, that bear no cautions, and if you are at all unsure, consult a qualified herbalist. Herbs also vary in terms of the strength of their active ingredients depending on such factors as soil quality, age, and time of collecting, so again, for treating anything other than common ailments, consult a qualified herbal practitioner. And if you are pregnant or already taking medication, it is essential that you first consult your doctor. With self-help there is always the danger of misdiagnosis, and your own remedies may cure one ailment but aggravate another condition, causing problems elsewhere. Once you are aware of the dangers, using herbs that you have grown in your garden to treat minor ailments is very satisfactory. You can also avoid the problem of inaccurate identification and guarantee the purity and freshness of your plants.

GROWING AND HARVESTING HERBS

Herbs, with their special fragrances, flavours, colours and textures are highly versatile plants and are a pleasure to grow. If you are a city dweller without a garden, growing herbs is an ideal way of appreciating and keeping in touch with nature's recurring cycles.

Herbs are essentially wild plants. The perennials are fairly hardy and easy to grow, and the annuals are also tolerant, requiring less attention than vegetables. Most herbs will grow in a variety of soils and situations but you will achieve better results by simulating the plant's natural habitat. Site must be taken into account: some herbs, such as angelica and mint, prefer shade, while those of Mediterranean origin, including sage, thyme, rosemary and lavender, need full sun. Shelter may also be necessary: rosemary and lavender, for instance, are susceptible to cold and wind, so choose a sheltered spot and protect them from frost during harsh winters. Most herbs are adaptable and will survive in well-drained garden soil. Mint and meadowsweet, however, flourish best in damp ground, while for those that grow on sunny Mediterranean hillsides, a dry, gravelly soil is ideal. Generally speaking, small-leaved herbs prefer a dry, sunny position, while larger-leaved plants need more shade and moisture. It is worth attempting to grow herbs even if your garden is not ideal in terms of site or soil. You can always prepare raised beds for better drainage, or grow herbs in terracotta pots. Adding compost

GROWING HERBS FROM SEED

Most herbs can be grown from seed, notably annuals and biennials. Some, like marigold, evening primrose and borage, are self-seeding. Seed may be sown indoors in trays or directly into the garden, providing the soil has warmed up sufficiently after winter. Most seeds germinate in the dark, so you will need to cover the seed with a thin layer of soil. The exceptions include chervil, dill, chamomile, angelica and lemon balm, which need light for successful germination so should not be covered, but pressed lightly on the surface of the soil. Generally speaking, large seeds need less light than small seeds and tiny seeds may be scattered on the surface.

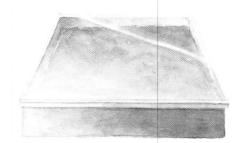

Parsley is notoriously difficult to grow from seed and requires a high temperature – 21°C (70°F) – for germination. Keep the surface of seed trays moist and cover with a sheet of glass or clear plastic, but remove it as soon as the seed begins to sprout.

will improve light, sandy soils. If you do not have a garden, you can still grow a reasonable range of herbs. Basil, parsley, mint, marjoram, dill, oregano, sage and winter savory can all be grown successfully indoors. Turn the plants regularly for an even distribution of light, and put those that prefer full sun

outside on the windowsill in warm weather. You can also plant herbs together in window boxes, but some, such as mint, are invasive and must be grown in separate pots.

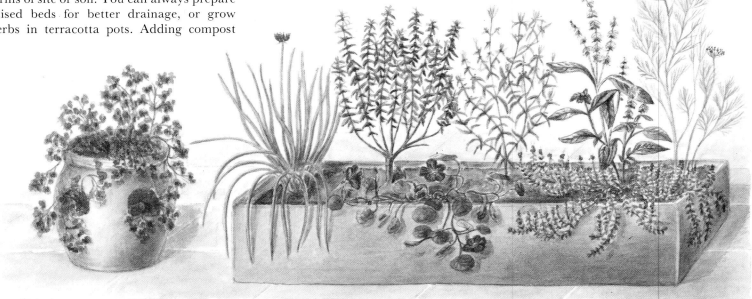

ROOT PROPAGATION AND DIVISION

Herbs that have creeping root systems, like mint and bergamot, are easy to propagate. In spring or autumn, cut a section from one of the horizontal roots or runners that spread from the main root, or simply divide the roots. Root division is also appropriate for herbs that have formed dense clumps, for example yarrow. Separate the roots with two garden forks, replant and water well. For herbs with fleshy roots, like horseradish and ginger, carefully uproot the plant and separate the roots with a sharp knife. Replant and water.

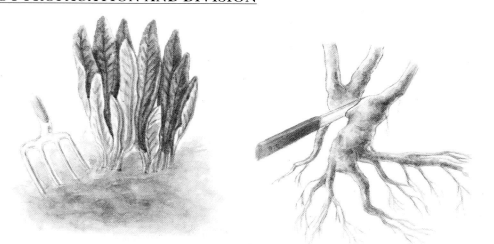

LAYERING

Herbs that do not have spreading roots, including sage, rosemary, thyme, hyssop and winter savory, can be propagated by layering. In spring take one of the older but not too rigid branches from the base of the plant and peg it down firmly into the soil, stripping off any foliage that would otherwise come into contact with the soil. Water regularly and when roots have formed, sever the old branch.

PROPAGATION FROM CUTTINGS

Herbs to grow from cuttings include sage, rosemary, lavender, marjoram, lemon verbena and thyme. Seed can produce variable plants but taking cuttings ensures that the new plant will have the same characteristics as the parent. French tarragon can only be grown from cuttings: seed is usually of the less aromatic Russian variety. Take cuttings from young, not woody, stems in late spring, severing just below the node – where the leaf joins the stem. Remove the lower leaves and plant in pots in moist potting compost mixed with sharp sand. Spray the cuttings with water and cover the pot with an upturned jar, or a polythene bag resting on sticks or a wire loop to prevent contact with the leaves. Keep the cuttings out of direct sunlight.

ORGANIC GARDENING

With herbs that will be eaten as food or medicine you may wish to avoid the use of chemical pesticides and fertilizers. Organic gardening methods, such as composting, mulching and crop rotation, aim to enrich and strengthen the soil so that it produces healthy plants with greater resistance to pests and diseases. Specific problems, such as aphid infestation, can be treated with natural alternatives to chemical pesticides, including derris, pyrethrum, quassia chips, an infusion of elder leaves, or soft soap. If you have a problem with slugs, make a slug trap by sinking a jar or can filled with stale beer in the ground.

COMPANION PLANTING

Traditional gardening wisdom maintains that many plants, particularly fragrant and aromatic herbs, have a beneficial or adverse effect on neighbouring plants. Culinary herbs are said to enhance the flavour of the vegetables or fruits that they are commonly paired with. Basil is reputed to improve the flavour of tomatoes, while summer savoury is beneficial for broad beans, and dill for cabbage. Herbs, however, are highly versatile plants and fulfil a dual function in the garden: their scent is also said to confuse and divert pests from vegetables and flowers. Plant garlic among roses to keep away aphids; and sage amongst cabbage to repel cabbage white butterflies. Curiously, sage, despite its culinary association with onions, is reputed to be of no benefit to these vegetables and may even harm them.

COLLECTING AND STORING HERBS

Some herbs can be picked throughout the growing season, while evergreens or deciduous perennials are available all year round. The leafy herbs are best picked just before the plant flowers, and in the morning when the dew has dried but before the oils have begun to evaporate in hot sun. Snip sprigs from the very ends of the stems to allow growth to continue, and try not to overpick and weaken the plant. Choose healthy sprigs and discard any yellowing leaves. If you are gathering herbs from the wild, make sure you have made a positive identification: mistaking foxglove leaves for comfrey can have fatal results. Avoid, too, collecting rate or endangered plants.

Use fresh herbs within a week: they keep well in sealed plastic bags in the refrigerator. If you intend to dry the herbs for winter use, start the process as soon as possible as the scent, flavour and health-giving properties begin to diminish as soon as they are separated from the parent plant.

Drying and storage foliage

Leafy herbs are traditionally preserved by drying, for culinary, cosmetic and medicinal use. Freezing herbs is quicker, but some herbalists feel this impairs the healing properties of the herb and prefer to use fresh or dried plants. Several culinary herbs are suitable for drying, including bay, sage, rosemary, thyme, mint, and oregano. Tarragon is more suitable for freezing. The key to successful drying is rapid reduction of the moisture content of the plant. The ideal temperature for the first 24 hours of drying is 32–34°C(90–93°F), then 24–26°C(75–80°F) for the next three to seven days. Maintaining such temperatures in the home is difficult but successful methods include an airing cupboard, or an oven on the lowest setting, with the door ajar. Keep herbs out of direct sunlight to prevent evaporation of essential oils. Bundles of herbs can be placed in paper bags, tied at the neck to keep out both sunlight and dust. Herbs are dry when they feel brittle and are easy to crumble. This may take between three to five days for leaves, five to ten days for bunches, and as little as one hour for oven-dried herbs. Store in airtight, dark glass

COMPANION PLANTING

HERB	HELPS	HINDERS
Anise	Coriander	–
Basil	Tomatoes, peppers	Rue
Bergamot	Tomatoes	–
Borage	Strawberries, tomatoes, beans	–
Caraway	Peas	Fennel
Chamomile	Cucumber, onions, most vegetables and herbs	–
Chervil	Radishes	–
Chives	Apple trees, carrots, roses, parsley	Beans, peas
Coriander	Anise, carrots, cabbage	Fennel
Dill	Cabbage, onions, lettuce, most vegetables	Tomatoes
Fennel	As for dill	Beans, peppers
Garlic	Roses	–
Horseradish	Potatoes	–
Hyssop	Grape vines, cabbage	Radishes
Lovage	Beans	–
Marigold (French)	Potatoes, tomatoes, roses	–
Mint	Cabbage family, tomatoes, most vegetables	–
Nasturtium	Most vegetables, particularly cabbage family, broad beans, tomatoes; also apple trees	–
Nettle	Most vegetables, herbs and fruits	–
Oregano	Beans, cabbage	–
Pennyroyal	Cabbage family, most vegetables	–
Rosemary	Carrots, cabbage family, beans, sage	Potatoes, rue
Rue	Figs	Basil, cabbage, sage
Sage	Cabbage family, carrots, tomatoes, strawberries	Onion
Summer Savory	Beans, onions	–
Tarragon	Most vegetables and herbs	–
Thyme	Potatoes, aubergines, tomatoes, cabbage	–
Wormwood	–	Most vegetables
Yarrow	Most herbs	–

jars, and crumble or rub the herbs through a sieve as you need them. You can also make up individual muslin bags filled with a bouquet garni mixture.

Drying and storing seeds

Gather seeds when they have ripened from green to brown or black and grown hard. Choose a dry day for collecting ripe pods and for shaking larger seeds off the plant and into paper bags. Some herbs, notably thyme, produce tiny seeds, while those of the borage family must be collected before they have a chance to fall to the ground. If you cannot examine plants every day, tie muslin or cheesecloth around the stem to catch the falling seeds. For best results, dry the seed indoors for two weeks to remove all traces of moisture.

When you have separated the seeds from the stems and pods, store them in air-tight jars and keep in a cool, dry place. Seeds that are intended for propagation are best stored in clearly labelled envelopes.

Drying and storing roots

Roots, since they are denser than foliage or seeds, absorb additional moisture from damp autumn soil, and take longer to dry. Dig up roots in the autumn when the growing season is over and foliage has died down. Lift the roots gently and cut a piece from the branches, leaving behind the central section. Remove any soil clinging to the root and scrub thoroughly in cold water, but do not leave the root immersed in water. Place small sections or slices of root on a baking tray in a slow oven set at 50–60°C(120–150°F) and turn frequently. When the pieces are easily broken they are ready to store in airtight, dark glass or ceramic jars, away from direct heat or sunlight.

Freezing Herbs

Freezing is a fast, convenient method for preserving the more delicate herbs that do not dry well, such as dill, parsley, chervil, fennel, chives, tarragon and possibly basil. As frozen herbs have a shorter storage life than dried herbs – six months – freeze those that you use most often in cooking. Freezing is not considered suitable for medicinal herbs. Some cooks recommend blanching herbs before storage to kill bacteria and preserve colour, but many consider this unnecessary. According to others, blanched herbs can be stored for up to six months, while non-blanched herbs should be used within two months.

When you have collected your chosen herbs, begin preparations for freezing as soon as possible. Always keep the different herbs separate so that the flavours of one type are not transferred to another. Divide the herbs into sprigs, or into quantities you would normally use in cooking, and put them into sealed, labelled and dated freezer bags. Another effective method is to chop or tear the herbs and put a small quantity of each into ice cube trays, Top up the trays with water or stock, freeze, and then store the cubes in labelled and dated freezer bags.

HERBS IN THE HOME

COOKING WITH HERBS

Today we make a clear distinction between culinary and medicinal herbs: for our ancestors there was no dividing line. Common vegetables originated in the wild and although the roots were eaten, they were also made into a healing poultice for ulcers and sores. Caraway seed, found in prehistoric sites, has been used for at least 5000 years. The Romans considered the seed an excellent digestive but are also reported to have made a bread from the mashed root. In Northern Europe fresh produce was virtually non-existent for most of the winter months so the young leaves of dock, sorrel and dandelion, were considered cleansing to the system as well as palatable after the monotonous winter diet of starchy and salty food. The use of spices was originally confined to the East but an international trade was established by 1550 BC. Spices were transported along caravan routes from China and Indonesia through the Middle East to the eastern Mediterranean. In the twelfth and thirteenth centuries, Italian merchants imported spices into Europe, and their native cities grew prosperous. Trade was effectively controlled by the Arab nations since the overland routes cut through their lands, but the enormous market value of spices motivated the discovery of sea routes to the East which effectively broke the Arab monopoly.

During the Middle Ages, herbs and spices had become indispensable for disguising rancid food or improving the taste of bland dishes. Following the discovery of the New World, more exotic herbs and spices, such as allspice and chillies, became available to Europeans. In sixteenth-century England, herbs, apart from the medicinal 'simples', were classified as pot herbs, 'sallet' herbs and sweet herbs. Pot herbs included leafy green and root vegetables, such as sorrel, onions and parsnips, and were boiled or roasted for their health-giving properties. 'Sallet' or salad herbs were often served raw and ranged from simple combinations of herbs and vegetables in a dressing to elaborate compositons known as 'grand sallets' that might feature roast meats, oysters, olives, capers, nuts, fruits and vegetables. Sweet herbs such as sweet marjoram, basil or cicely were employed purely to enhance the flavour of a particular dish, in the same manner as we use kitchen herbs today.

In recent years, foreign travel, together with access to the different styles of cooking and flavouring offered by immigrants from other cultures, has re-awakened popular interest in herbs. The wonderful variety and increased availability of herbs has encouraged many people to introduce dishes incorporating different flavours into their culinary repertoire. The growing disenchantment with artificial flavourings and colourings has motivated many people to turn to natural herbal flavours, while herbs and spices can reduce the amount of salt or sugar commonly used to season or sweeten food.

Cooking with herbs is a matter of experience, good judgement, personal taste, and a grasp of the basics. The flavour and strength of herbs varies according to freshness and soil quality, so it is impossible to lay down rules as to quantities and combinations: it depends on your palate. It is generally accepted, however, that dried herbs have a more pronounced flavour than fresh, and some, such as oregano and thyme, must be used sparingly or they will overpower, rather than enhance, your cooking. Using herbs and spices in dishes destined for the freezer also calls for restraint since the flavours increase in strength during storage.

Fresh herbs

The flavour of most leafy culinary herbs is due to the fragrant essential oils, and since these are volatile and evaporate with heat, it is best to pick herbs as you need them. If you are using bought herbs, store in the refrigerator in a sealed plastic bag or box so that the leaves do not dry out. Bruised, whole leaves or sprigs are used in marinades, and for rubbing joints of meat, but most recipes call for chopped herbs. Some cooks advise tearing or snipping, as chopping some herbs, such as basil, can impair their flavour. Many herbs lose their flavour with long cooking or boiling, particularly such delicate-flavoured herbs as sweet marjoram, chervil and dill. It is better to use these only in lightly cooked dishes, and to add them at the last minute. More robust herbs, such as oregano and thyme, will hold their flavour in dishes with longer cooking times, and long, slow cooking in sealed casseroles or pans can improve the flavour and aroma of the dish. With the exception of the very delicate and the more pungent herbs, it is advisable with dishes that require lengthy cooking, or sauces that require boiling, to add herbs only during the last 10 to 15 minutes.

The following mixtures are intended as a starting point. Begin cautiously until you are well acquainted with the subtle flavours of herbs, then experiment with confidence and discover combinations that are to your own personal taste.

Bouquet garni This classic mixture is used in soups, casseroles and sauces, and is removed before serving. Tie together with string three parsley stalks, a sprig of thyme and a bay leaf. Other variations include adding a sprig of marjoram, or changing the proportions of thyme to parsley. The herbs can also be enclosed in two pieces of celery, bound with string, or tied in a muslin bag.

Fines herbes In French cuisine this mixture of delicate herbs is the classic seasoning for omelettes and some sauces. It consists of four parts snipped fresh parsley to two parts each of chives, chervil and tarragon. Use it at once and add in the last minutes of cooking. You can also vary this mixture and use it to flavour softened butter or low-fat soft cheese, or mayonnaise.

Herb vinegars To each bottle (500ml/17.5fl oz) of white wine or apple cider vinegar (some recipes advise you to warm the vinegar first), add four large sprigs of tarragon, basil, rosemary, dill, thyme or fennel. You can also use peeled garlic cloves or chillies. Stand the sealed bottle in a warm place and turn every day for two weeks. Strain and taste for strength; if you prefer a stronger taste, add two fresh sprigs and repeat the process. You can also include a sprig for decorative purposes and to identify the vinegar, but the taste will become even more pronounced. Use infused vinegar in sauces, stocks, marinades, and salad dressings. The vinegar will keep for at least 12 months.

Herb oils Use a good quality mild oil, such as sunflower, or olive oil if you prefer a stronger-flavoured oil. Add bruised sprigs of your chosen herb in quantities of roughly one part herb to eight parts oil, and follow the method given above for herb vinegar. Test for flavour and replace the herb if necessary. Oils flavoured with basil, marjoram, thyme, rosemary or garlic are particularly good in salad dressings, marinades, and stir-fries. If you begin by gradually incorporating flavoured oils into your cooking you will soon be able to judge their individual potencies. Use within two to three months.

Herb honey Flavour jars of warmed honey be adding bruised fresh rose petals, sage leaves, a sprig of thyme, or lemon balm. As with herb vinegar and oil, leave in a warm position and turn daily for a week. Strain and use.

Dill sauce In a heavy-based pan melt 100g (4oz) butter over a gentle heat until it begins to foam. Remove the pan from the heat and slowly stir in 1 tbsp double cream and 50g (2oz) chopped, fresh dill. Season to taste and serve warm with poached fish, new potatoes, steamed courgettes or any spring or summer vegetable.

Pesto sauce Put the following into a blender: 50g (2oz) fresh basil leaves (minus stalks); 50g (2oz) pine kernels; 100ml (4fl.oz) olive oil; 3 crushed garlic cloves; and 25g (2oz) grated parmesan. Blend until you have a thick smooth purée. Serve with pasta, or in aubergine dishes. Store in a sealed glass jar, in a cool, dark place.

Fresh flowers

You can create subtle fragrances and flavours, and enhance the visual appeal of summer drinks and salads by adding colourful herb blossoms. Float blue borage flowers in wine cups and include fresh sprigs of woodruff. Elder flowers make excellent sweet fritters and rose-petal jam is popular in Eastern Europe and the Middle East. Crystallized violets make an attractive, edible decoration for cakes and puddings.

Flower salads The petals from marigold (calendula) heads add an unusual, sweetish taste to rice salads and green salads as well as looking attractive. Include fresh nasturtium petals in green salads for a dash of colour and to give the dish a peppery taste. Other edible blossoms suitable for inclusion in salads are chive flowers, bergamot, mint, rose and violet. When using fresh flowers however, choose a mild salad dressing that will not overpower their delicate flavour.

Dried herbs

Some herbs are unsuitable for drying including dill, parsley, chives, and fennel, while the flavour of others, notably basil, is

COOKING WITH HERBS

Angelica	Crystallized stems in cakes; fresh leaves in fruit dishes
Anise	Fresh leaves in soups and salads
Basil	Fresh leaves in pasta dishes; in pesto sauce; with tomatoes and mushrooms
Bay	Dried leaf in bouquet garni; in soups, stocks, stews; with fish
Borage	Fresh young leaves in soups and salads; flowers in salads; flowers and leaves in wine cups
Caraway	Seed in bread, cakes, biscuits; with cabbage, parsnips, beetroot
Celery seed	In sauces and savoury biscuits; in curries and pickles
Chervil	Fresh leaves in *fines herbes;* in egg dishes, salads soups, sauces
Chives	Chopped fresh leaves with soft cheeses; in salads, soups; in omelettes
Coriander	Fresh leaves in salads, especially carrot; seed in curries, chutneys and fresh leaf as a garnish
Dill	Fresh leaves with fish; in sauces and marinades for fish; in soups, salads; with potatoes, courgettes, marrow; seed in pickles; in bread and cakes
Fennel	Fresh leaves with fish and poultry; with soft cheeses; seed with oily fish; in sauces, soups; in teas
Garlic	Fresh bulb in Mediterranean cookery; in soups, casseroles, sauces, dressings, dips, mayonnaise
Ginger	Fresh root in stir-fries, curries; fresh or dried root in chutneys and pickles; dried, ground root in fruit dishes, cakes and biscuits; stem ginger in fruit salads
Horseradish	Fresh, grated root in sauces for beef, fish, shellfish
Hyssop	Fresh leaves in salads, fruit dishes
Lemon balm	Fresh leaves in fruit salads; in sweet and savoury sauces; in stuffings; in wine cups
Lemon verbena	Fresh leaves in fruit salads, fruit punches; in teas
Lovage	Fresh leaves in soups, casseroles; with poultry; in salads
Marigold	Fresh petals in soups; in salads; with soft cheeses
Marjoram	Fresh or dried leaves in bouquet garni; in soups and casseroles; with tomatoes and beans; in meat and poultry dishes
Mint	Fresh leaves in Middle Eastern cookery; with yoghurt; in sauces for lamb; in summer drinks and fruit salads; in teas
Nasturtium	Fresh petals in green salads; with soft cheeses
Oregano	Fresh or dried leaves in most Italian dishes, particularly pasta sauces and pizza; with meat dishes; with tomatoes, mushrooms and aubergines
Parsley	Fresh leaves in bouquet garni; in soups, sauces, casseroles; in butters; in salads; extensively used as a garnish
Rosemary	Whole fresh sprigs with lamb or poultry
Sage	Fresh or dried leaves in stuffings with onion, for fatty meats; in sausages; with cheeses
Savory, Summer	Fresh or dried with beans, lentils and peas; in soups
Sweet Cicely	Fresh leaves with stewed fruit, in fruit salads
Sorrel	Fresh leaves in sauces for fish; in soups
Tarragon	Fresh or dried leaves with poultry and fish; in vinegars, sauces, dressings; in omelettes and with mushrooms
Thyme	Fresh or dried leaves in bouquet garni; in stews, meat dishes; with tomatoes and courgettes; lemon thyme with fruit
Watercress	Fresh leaves in soups; in sauces for fish; in salads

much impaired by the drying process. Dried herbs also lose both scent and taste, becoming hay-like when kept for longer than three to six months. With dried home-grown herbs you can, of course, guarantee both quality and freshness. Certain herbs, specifically bay and oregano are, however, improved with drying and are rarely used fresh. You can bring out the flavour of dried herbs by first steeping them in a little of the liquid, either vinegar, lemon juice or oil, that your dish requires. A recent culinary innovation is freeze-dried herbs which, although considerably more expensive than conventionally-dried herbs, better retain both flavour and colour, and resemble fresh herbs once they have absorbed some of the cooking liquid. You will also need smaller quantities of freeze-dried herbs: approximately 1 teaspoon of freeze-dried to one tablespoon of dried.

Spices

Powdered spices are considered inferior in flavour to the freshly ground variety. Buy whole spices and grind as needed using a small spice mill for such hard spices as juniper, cardamon, and coriander, and use a peppermill for allspice and mustard seed, as well as peppercorns. Nutmeg and dried, whole ginger can be finely grated. Sweet dishes often call for ground ginger, which, like the other very hard spices such as cinnamon sticks or turmeric root, is easier to buy already ground, although it can be reduced to a powder in a coffee mill and sieved. Fresh ginger is ideal for oriental dishes and curries and is peeled and crushed, using a garlic press or a pestle and mortar. When making marinades, stocks, and pickles, leave spices whole and strain if necessary. Some cooks advocate dry roasting spices in a heavy pan for a more pronounced, aromatic flavour when preparing curries and other highly-spiced dishes.

Spice mixtures

Hot curry powder Grind together as many of the following spices as you wish:

1 tbsp coriander seed (essential), 2 dried red chillies, 1 tsp fenugreek seeds, 1 tsp black mustard seeds, 1 tsp cloves, 1 tbsp peeled brown cardamon seeds, 5cm (2in) stick of cinnamon, 1 tsp black cumin seeds, 1 tsp turmeric powder.

To improve the flavour of this powder, first dry roast the spices in a medium oven (160°C, 325°F, Gas 3) for 10 minutes before grinding to a powder. This mixture will keep for up to three months in an airtight container.

Garam masala There are many variations of this sweet spice mixture including the following:

1 tbsp coriander seeds, 1 tbsp brown cardamom seeds, 1 tsp black cumin seeds, 1 tsp cloves, 1 tsp black peppercorns, 5cm (2in) stick cinnamon and 1 tsp blade of mace. First dry roast the spices in a medium oven (160°C, 325°F, Gas 3) for 10 minutes, then grind to a powder. Store in an airtight container after use.

Pickling spice This mixture commonly includes dried red chillies, black peppercorns, mustard seed, whole allspice, cloves and ginger, but coriander, dill and celery seed, plus garlic, can also be used.

HERBAL COSMETICS

The use of herbs as beauty aids can be traced back to the earliest civilizations. Five thousand years ago, the ancient Egyptians were colouring their hair with a mixture of henna and indigo, and scenting it with marjoram. In the first century AD, the original moisturizing skin cream based on olive oil, beeswax and rose water was created by the celebrated Greek physician Galen. Herbal essences have always been popular for perfuming the skin, for massage, and for bathing. In recent years, partly in response to a range of adverse reactions caused by harsh chemically-based skin and hair preparations, there has been a widespread revival in gentler herbal cosmetics, many of them based on traditional recipes going back centuries. The manufacture of leading herb-based cosmetics does not involve animal testing and, in common with that of herbal medicines, creates less environmental pollution. Used regularly, herbal preparations can improve both skin and hair, but for best results consider adopting a more holistic approach to health that takes into account lifestyle and diet. Herbs, too, have a part to play in our emotional well-being. The fragrances released by the essential oils in plants directly affect the brain, and certain essences can uplift us or bring relaxation. Well-loved herbs, such as lavender, with their clean, fresh scent can also reawaken memories of past experiences.

Infusions

Basic infusion 1–1½ handfuls of fresh herbs or 1 tbsp dried herbs to 600ml(1pt) of still spring water.

Strong infusion 3 handfuls of fresh herbs or 2 tbsp dried to 600ml(1pt) of spring water.

An infusion is made like a tea. Put your chosen herbs into a clean china, glass, or enamel bowl or teapot. Add boiling spring water, cover, steep for 20 to 30 mins. Strain and use. The infusion will keep for three days in the fridge.

Decoction

Basic decoction 28g(1oz) of herbs to 600ml (1pt) of still spring water.

This method is traditionally used for the tougher parts of herbs, such as roots or woody stems. You can also make a decoction from dried herbs if a stronger, more concentrated preparation is called for. Chop the herb material into small pieces, if necessary, and put into an enamelled pan with the spring water. Bring to the boil, cover and simmer for 20 minutes. Strain, cool, and use. The decoction will keep for three days in the fridge.

Bathing with herbs

For a *relaxing* herbal bath, add to bathwater that is not too hot, a strong infusion or decoction of chamomile, jasmine or lime flowers, or vervain (aerial parts).

For a *stimulating* bath, add a strong infusion or decoction of rosemary, lemon verbena, or pine needles.

Other ways of incorporating herbs into your baths include adding two drops of your chosen herb's essential oil to the bathwater, or making a bath bag with added skin-softening properties. Fill a muslin bag or handkerchief with ½ cup of fine oatmeal to 1–1½ cups of fresh or ¾ cup of dried herbs. Tie up the bag, let it soak in your bathwater, and rub it over your face and body when you have finished soaking.

Soaps Soap made with naturally fragrant herbs is gentler on the skin than the artificially perfumed variety, and is less likely to dry it out. Choose a herb and an essential oil appropriate for your own skin type and follow this basic recipe for herbal soap.

Take the following: 170g(6oz) grated unscented, uncoloured, very mild soap; 120g(4oz) dried or 4 handfuls of fresh herbs, simmered in 375ml (1–1½ cups) water in a covered pan and left overnight to infuse; 1 tsp essential oil.

Put the grated soap into a basin over a pan

of gently simmering water and stir in the strained herbal infusion. Whisk vigorously until all the soap has melted. Remove from the heat and add the essential oil. Pour the soap into small, greased moulds or waxed paper cake cases and leave to cool. Wrap the soap in greaseproof paper and leave in a warm place, such as an airing cupboard, for six to eight weeks. If you have sensitive skin, replace 85g(3oz) of the soap with the same amount of honey. Add the honey when the soap is beginning to melt.

Herbs for skin care

For cleansing the skin, dab on an infusion of elder flowers, sweet violet, marigold blossom, or yarrow.

For toning the skin, use an infusion of thyme, and for their astringent properties dab on an infusion of witch hazel, meadowsweet, or lady's mantle. Marigold and yarrow are herbs with both cleansing and toning properties.

Facial steam For deep cleaning try a facial steam choosing herbs from the list below according to your skin type. Do not try a facial steam if you have very dry or very sensitive skin, or if you suffer from asthma.

First cleanse your skin and tie back your hair. Then measure 2 handfuls of fresh leaves or flowers (or 3 tbsp dried herbs) into a bowl or basin. Pour on 1.8l(3pt) boiling water and stir. Using a towel, make a tent over your head and around the bowl to keep in the steam, keeping your face at a comfortable distance from the basin. Maintain this position, with your eyes closed, for five to ten minutes, then remove the towel and apply a cool flannel or towel to your face.

Herbs for normal to dry skin Lime or chamomile blossom, violet leaves and flowers, elderflowers, parsley, borage, marshmallow leaves and roots.
Herbs for oily skin Lavender or marigold flowers, yarrow, lady's mantle, witch hazel, horsetail.
Herbs to improve circulation Rosemary, nettle, fennel.

Herbs for hair care
Shampoos You can make your own herbal shampoo by adding a few drops of an essential oil suitable for your hair to a bottle of very mild unperfumed shampoo; or add a tablespoon of a strong decoction or infusion of your chosen herb to your usual amount of shampoo, mixing the two in a cup. For an entirely herbal shampoo based on soapwort, try the following recipe:

BATHING WITH HERBS

Take herbal baths by adding a strong infusion or decoction of your chosen herbs, or two to three drops of a herbal essential oil to your bathwater. For times when you are tired, anxious, stressed or sleepless, choose herbs that have a relaxing effect; if you need a boost or have a busy day or evening ahead, choose herbs for their stimulating effect. Use the table below as a guide.

HERB	RELAXING	STIMULATING
Basil		●
Chamomile	●	
Comfrey	●	
Jasmine	●	
Lavender	●	
Lemon verbena		●
Lime flowers	●	
Marigold	●	
Peppermint		●
Pine		●
Rosemary		●
Vervain (aerial parts)	●	

30g(1oz) bruised and shredded soapwort root 1l (2pts) still spring or filtered water, Bring the soapwort root and water to the boil in a covered pan and simmer for 20 minutes. Cool, strain and use. This shampoo will produce much less lather than soap or detergent-based shampoos, but it is an effective cleanser and suitable for all hair types.

Hair and scalp conditioners To stimulate hair growth prepare a strong infusion of nettle, rosemary or horsetail. Strain and cool, and massage the infusion well into the scalp after washing. For best results, after massaging your scalp with the infusion, wrap your head in a warm towel and wait for five to ten minutes before drying your hair.

Make a strong infusion of your chosen herb (using the list below), strain into a jug and keep warm. After washing your hair in the usual manner, pour over the infusion, catch the liquid in a basin and repeat three or four times. Adding an acidic preparation

to your final rinsing water after washing, will impart shine to your hair. For dark hair, add 2 tsp of rosemary vinegar (see page 14); for fair hair add 2 tsp of freshly squeezed lemon juice.

For fair to blonde hair Chamomile or elderflowers
For brunettes and dark hair Rosemary, sage, thyme
For redheads Marigold flowers, henna

Natural hair colourings Powdered henna leaf has been employed as a hair and skin colouring for around 5000 years. It coats and conditions the hair shaft, and imparts copper or auburn tones to hair that ranges in colour from mid-brown through to black, gradually fading over a few months. Applying henna to light brown hair usually produces orange tones. Persian henna is thought to be superior to Egyptian. Mix 1 cupful of powdered henna leaf with 1 teaspoon of cider or wine vinegar and enough boiling water to make a thick, stiff paste.

While the mixture cools, apply moisturizing cream to your hairline to avoid staining your skin and wear rubber gloves. Then divide your hair into sections and apply the paste. Cover your hair with plastic film or foil and wrap a towel (preferably an old one) around your head to keep in the heat. Test for colour strength after 30 minutes, but leave for between one and two hours for deeper shades. Rinse off the henna and shampoo in the usual way.

Hair darkener If you have black to dark brown hair that is greying, you can achieve a darker effect using black walnut shells and leaves. First soak a generous handful of crushed, unripe husks and leaves, together with a pinch of salt, in enough water to cover for three days. Then put the liquid into an enamelled pan, add a further three cups of water and boil until one cup of liquid remains. Strain and use as a final hair rinse, wearing rubber gloves. Catch the liquid in a basin and repeat four or five times. Blot your hair dry with an old towel as the liquid may stain. Used regularly, this stain will result in a dark brown tone.

HOUSEHOLD HERBS

Herbal air fresheners

In Medieval times, strewing herbs, such as santolina, lady's bedstraw and lavender, were scattered over the floor to sweeten the air and disguise offensive odours. Our modern, chemical-based air fresheners achieve the same effect but by simply overpowering unpleasant smells with a strong, synthetic scent. Some work by temporarily impairing your sense of smell. Herbs and essential oils provide safe, natural air fresheners. Grow aromatic plants such as scented geraniums – the fresh scent is released if you gently brush the leaves with your hand – and bring pots of evergreen herbs like rosemary indoors in the winter. If you live in the country, hang up bunches of sweet woodruff: the vanilla-scented leaves freshened the air of Medieval churches on feast days. A vase filled with wild or cultivated honeysuckle, too, will fill the room with a rich, sweet fragrance.

Essential oils Pure essential oils can be burned in ceramic incensors to fill a room with a favourite smell, or you can simply add three or four drops to a small dish of water placed near a radiator or heat source. Try using essentials oils such as sandalwood to create a relaxing atmosphere, or choose lavender or lemon for a clean, fresh smell.

There are various methods of extracting the essential oils from herbs, the most common being steam distillation. For successful results, professional expertize and such specialist equipment as retorts and condensers are required, so it is impractical to attempt to make your own essential oils at home.

One method of extracting the oil, however, known as maceration, can be carried out with confidence, although the resulting oil will not be as pure or concentrated as professionally prepared oils.

Take the following: ½l(1pt) sweet almond oil; 1 tbsp cider vinegar; 1 heaped handful of your chosen fresh herb; large preserving jar, sterilized.

Pound the herb in a pestle and mortar, and put into the preserving jar. Pour over the oil and add the cider vinegar. Make sure that the jar is not full as you will need to shake the mixture daily. Put the jar in a warm, sunny window and shake vigorously every day for at least a month. Strain through a nylon sieve and bottle in a clean, dark glass jar. If the oil is not strong enough, repeat the process using the same batch of oil but a fresh supply of herbs.

Herbal disinfectants Some essential oils have both deodorizing and disinfecting properties. Add a few drops of essential oil of pine, juniper, or eucalyptus to the toilet bowl instead of harsh, chemical, toilet-freshener blocks. You can also make a strong infusion of eucalyptus, thyme, pine needles or rosemary, and use it to wipe down bathroom surfaces and clean the toilet bowl. Herbal disinfectants are milder than bleach- or phenol-based proprietary brands.

Pot pourri Traditionally pot pourris, or rotten pots, were made by fermenting sweet scented plant material with salt and orris root in covered jars. Elizabethan recipes also included spices and brandy. The orris root and salt act as fixatives to stabilize and preserve the fragrance. Today, most pot pourris are prepared according to the dry method since it is easier and less time-consuming. Moist pot pourris keep their fragrance longer than dried mixtures but the fermented material is not as attractive to look at, so keep them in ceramic jars, not open bowls. One suggestion for prolonging the life of dry pot pourri is to put the mixture in a bowl or wide-necked jar with a lid, opening it only when you want to perfume the air. Dry pot pourris are, however, very decorative so you could compromise by covering the container only when the room is not occupied. As long as the leaves and petals in your pot-pourri have not faded, you can revive the scent by adding a few drops of a complementary essential oil. There are no fixed rules for pot pourri mixtures so choose leaves, flowers and spices according to your own preferences. Instructions for drying herbs are given on pages 12–13.

Floral mixtures
Lavender
Rose
Carnation
Chamomile
Elderflowers
Nasturtium
Honeysuckle
Lily of the Valley
Jasmine

Herb leaf mixtures
Lemon verbena
Rosemary
Sage
Marjoram
Lemon balm
Bay
Thyme

Spices
Cloves (whole)
Cinnamon
Nutmeg
Allspice
Coriander seed

Traditional moist pot pourri There are various complicated old recipes for making this long-lasting pot pourri. It is traditionally based on either rose petals alone, or a mixture of rose petals, bay leaves, lemon verbena leaves and lavender flowers. The method is to start with a layer of the dried petals, sprinkle over a small handful of salt and press down well. Repeat this procedure until you have filled a wide-necked jar. Store the mixture under pressure using a weighted lid, saucer, or plate, and leave in a dark, dry place for two weeks or until the mixture has solidified. Then break up the resulting 'cake' into small pieces and mix with sweet, powdered spices, such as allspice and cloves. Return the mixture to the jar and leave it for three to six weeks, or, for best results, for a further six months. The mixture can now be transferred to a ceramic container ready for use. Some recipes advise adding a few drops of brandy if the mixture has dried out.

Dry pot pourri Assemble in a large bowl enough dried flower petals or leaves to fill your chosen container. Stir in any combination of such spices as whole cloves, broken cinnamon sticks, ground allspice or cinnamon. For a herbal, as opposed to a floral pot pourri, select dried aromatic leaves, omitting the spices if you prefer. Now add two tbsps of sea salt and two tbsps of powdered orris root, and a tsp of a single, or a combination, of your preferred essential oils. Mix together with a wooden spoon (metal may impair the fragrance) and transfer the mixture to a wide-necked jar. Cover tightly and store in a dark, dry place for three to six weeks, shaking the jar about once a week to ensure even blending. The pot pourri is now ready for use.

Insect repellants
Proprietary insect repellants such as fly spray, ant-killer, and moth-proofer commonly contain chemicals that give off irritating fumes. Herbal preparations offer effective and safer alternatives.

Indoors Many leafy aromatic herbs, notably tansy, mint, pennyroyal, wormwood and mugwort, have fly-repelling properties. Basil, too, is said to deter flies, and it was once traditional in parts of the Mediterranean to place pots of the small-leaved variety on the outside tables of Mediterranean cafes. In summer, jars or pots of these pungent-smelling herbs will help to keep your kitchen free from flying insects.

Pennyroyal is said to deter ants as well as flies. Rub sprigs around the ants' entry point or on kitchen worktops. A strong decoction of walnut leaves painted around door frames and skirting boards, will also keep ants out, or try dried chilli or paprika.

Southernwood – *garde robe* in French – is a traditional moth repellant, so too are lavender, rosemary, mugwort and pyrethrum flowers. Make sachets from the dried herbs and store them with woollens.

Cloves have long been used to deter moths, and a pomander or clove-studded orange is traditionally hung in the wardrobe. The moths are kept at bay by its strong, spicy aroma. The origin of the word pomander is French – *pomme d'ambre* or amber apple – and pomanders were originally made from a ball of ambergris encased in such materials as gold, silver, or bone and worn around the neck to dispel bad odours. Make your own pomander by drying a firm-skinned orange in an airing cupboard or other warm place for two or three days. Then push into the rind enough whole cloves to cover the surface. Roll the orange in a mixture of powdered cinnamon, nutmeg, and orris root, wrap in greaseproof paper and leave in a warm, dry place for two to three weeks. Once you have shaken off any surplus powder the pomander is ready to use.

Outdoors Rub elder leaves over your face, neck and arms to repel gnats, or make a strong infusion of the leaves and dab it on your skin as necessary. Essential oil of lavender also acts as an insect repellant, while oil of citronella is a well-known mosquito deterrent.

Herb pillows
Sweet-scented, dried herbs were once widely employed as mattress and pillow stuffings. Herbs were chosen not only for their fragrance but for their soothing and even aphrodisiac effect. You can make your own herbal pillow by stuffing a square of muslin with dried herbs that will fit a small pillow case, or alternatively make a smaller sachet and insert this, beside your usual pillow, into a standard size pillow case.

Soothing pillow
4 parts dried hop flowers
1 part lime flowers and sweet woodruff, mixed

Hops are a well-known soporofic and can help those with sleeping difficulties.

Fragrant pillow
3 parts dried meadowsweet
2 parts dried rose petals
2 parts dried agrimony

Meadowsweet has a sweet, honey-like scent which combines well with the perfume of the roses and the fruity smell of agrimony.

Fabric shampoo
Modern detergent-based cleaners are considered too harsh for old and delicate furnishings, or antique silk and lace. Soapwort, as its name suggests, is a gentle herbal alternative that has been used for washing wool since Medieval times. The fresh stems, and especially the root, contain lather-forming saponins that both clean and condition natural fabrics. Soapwort is ideal for cleaning tapestries and you can also follow the Middle Eastern practice of using it on vegetable-dyed woollen fabrics, such as rugs. Taking the whole fresh plant, first bruise the root and coarsely chop the stems. Boil the plant in enough filtered water to cover for 20 to 30 minutes, then strain and use. Dried soapwort root also works well but soak it in water overnight before boiling. After washing in soapwort solution, rinse the fabric in the usual way.

Aconite

Aconitum napellus

Ranunculaceae

Monkshood, wolf's bane, helmet flower

Aconite, especially the root, contains a group of deadly poisonous alkaloids. People have died through mistaking the leaves for parsley or the root for horseradish. A drug prepared from aconite was once employed as a pain reliever for neuralgia and sciatica. The precision of dosage required, however, left no margin for error and this led to its exclusion from both the US and the UK pharmacopeias. Aconite is still the source of an official Chinese drug and, in minute dose, an important homeopathic remedy.

The name aconite is derived from the Greek *akontion*, meaning dart, a reference to its former use by the Chinese as an arrow poison. Wolf's bane, the plant's other common name, is said to refer to the old practice of killing wolves either with arrows dipped in poisonous aconite juice, or in traps smeared with it. In Shakespeare's day aconite was popularly known as Monkshood because of the striking helmet-like shape of the flower. According to Greek myth, Hecate created aconite from the foaming mouth of Cerberus, the three-headed dog that guarded the entrance to the underworld. Hecate's daughter Medea was also aware of the lethal properties of aconite and attempted to poison Theseus, hero of ancient Greece, with it.

Aconite's deadly powers appear to have been exploited exclusively by women: according to one apocryphal tale, women could build up an immunity to its poison by eating minute doses from childhood and then pass it on to their sexual partners with lethal results. Witches, too, employed aconite, in combination with belladonna, to prepare their 'flying ointment'. Aconite is a hallucinogen that produces tingling sensations in the limbs, while belladonna causes delirium – a powerful and often fatal concoction. Although the herb was included in English plant lists from the tenth century, aconite was not used medicinally until the late eighteenth century.

CAUTION All parts of the plant are poisonous, especially the root. For professional use only.

HABITAT Native to the mountainous regions of Europe, particularly the Swiss Alps and the Pyrenees. Grows wild in open woods and on wooded mountain slopes, preferring moist soils and shade. Cultivated in Europe and North America.

DESCRIPTION Herbaceous perennial, but roots produce flowers in alternate years. Erect stem to 90cm(3ft) with dark green, glossy, palmate leaves that have jagged teeth. Distinctive purple, violet or blue flowers appear in terminal spikes during summer and autumn. The upper petal (actually a sepal) takes the form of a hood or helmet that fits closely over the rest of the flower. The root is fleshy and turnip shaped.

Agrimony
Agrimonia eupatoria

Rosaceae
Church steeples, cocklebur

Agrimony is an important herb that has been in domestic use for centuries to promote the healing of wounds and to stop bleeding. The botanical name *agrimonia* is derived from a Greek word signifying a plant beneficial for cataracts and failing eyesight. The herb does, in fact, make an effective eyewash. *Eupatoria*, the specific name, is in honour of Mithridates Eupator, a celebrated herbalist and king of ancient Persia, who devoted much of his time to the study of poisons and their antidotes. The Anglo Saxons considered agrimony an excellent wound-healing herb and also employed it for snake bites. For internal bleeding, a curious mixture consisting of the fresh plant pounded up with human blood and the flesh of frogs was recommended. The plant's association with ritual magic is also evident from the old belief that a person who slept with agrimony under the pillow would not wake up until the herb was removed. In fifteenth-century France, agrimony was an important ingredient of a healing water known as *arquebusade* that was used to treat the wounds of those hit with an arquebus, or old-fashioned hand gun. In sixteenth-century England wounds were commonly treated with a mixture of agrimony, or egrimoyne, mugwort and vinegar. Agrimony was also a traditional North American Indian remedy for fevers.

Modern herbalists consider agrimony beneficial for toning the digestive system and for easing indigestion and colitis. It is also recommended for gallstones, a traditional use since the time of the sixteenth-century surgeon and herbalist Gerard, who prescribed agrimony for 'naughty livers'. In Chinese herbal medicine, agrimony is recommended for excessive menstrual flow, while in European folk medicine a lotion or ointment may be used externally to speed up the healing of wounds. Both uses of the herb attest to its astringency, a property that also explains the herb's usefulness in cosmetic herbal preparations to tone the skin. Another traditional use of the plant is in agrimony water, a soothing gargle that was once said to be popular with singers and public speakers.

HABITAT Widespread throughout Europe, in parts of Asia, and in North America, especially the mountain slopes of southern California and in Arizona. Grows on waste ground, roadsides, along field edges and in hedgerows.

DESCRIPTION Graceful perennial with downy to rough reddish stems from 30–60cm(1–2ft). Its numerous leaves are divided into pairs that are oblong, toothed, deep green and downy, with a slight apple scent. Yellow, aromatic, five-petalled flowers appear from June to August, packed closely together in elongated spikes. They are followed by bristly, hooked seeds.

Alfalfa

Medicago sativa

Leguminosae

Lucerne, buffalo herb

For centuries alfalfa has been an important plant, and was thought to have been first discovered growing in Medea, North Africa. The name *medicago* means from Medea, while *sativa* means cultivated. Alfalfa has been grown since ancient times by Arab races as a fodder crop for their horses. It was imported into Greece and features in Roman writings but was not introduced into Europe until the seventeenth century. Around this period the plant acquired its common name, lucerne, from the Latin word for lamp – a reference to its shining seeds. Agriculturally, alfalfa has also been fed to cows to increase their milk yield. Medicinally, alfalfa was drunk as a tea to promote appetite and its diuretic action (increasing the flow of urine) is beneficial for urinary problems and water retention. Native Americans once employed the seed as an abortefacient.

Alfalfa has recently enjoyed a revival of interest due to the high nutritional value of its sprouted seeds. The vitamin and mineral content of plants at the sprouting stage is much higher than that of the mature plant and alfalfa is particularly rich in vitamin C, as well as B_1, B_2, K, chlorophyll and amino acids. Alfalfa can be sprouted easily at home and is ready to eat in five or six days, or buy it ready sprouted from greengrocers and health food stores. It makes a delicious and very nutritious addition to sandwiches and salads.

HABITAT Native to the Mediterranean and western Asia, naturalized in North America. Found wild on the edges of fields and in low-lying valleys as an escape from cultivation. Widely cultivated as far as Iran and Peru as a fodder crop.

DESCRIPTION A perennial with a deep taproot that penetrates 9–30m(30–100ft) deep, and has an upright, extensively branched stem 30cm–1m(12in–3ft) in height. Leaves are oval, grouped in threes, and growth is abundant. Numerous erect spikes of blue or violet flowers that resemble clover appear from June to August, followed by hairy seed pods in coiled spirals.

Allspice

Pimenta dioica, Pimenta officinalis

Myrtaceae

Jamaica pepper, myrtle pepper

Allspice is a common kitchen spice that is usually bought already ground, giving rise to the erroneous belief that it is a mixture of several spices. The name was invented in the late seventeenth century to describe the taste – a mixture of cinnamon, cloves, nutmeg and pepper. Jamaica supplies most of the world demand, hence the common name Jamaica pepper, and the island's numerous allspice trees form large tracts of natural woodland, also known as Pimento walks. The Latin name *pimenta* is derived from the Spanish word for pepper, because the ripe fruits resemble peppercorns.

Allspice contains a pungent volatile oil and was once used medicinally in the form of oil of Pimento to aid digestion and ease flatulence. Today the herb is chiefly employed as a spice and a condiment although, like other spices, it helps to alleviate wind and colic. The whole spice is commonly used for pickling, for example in the marinated raw herring of Scandinavian cuisine or in pickled onions. Ground allspice may be used in savoury dishes such as spiced meats, although it is more popularly employed in sweet dishes, from cakes and biscuits to milk puddings. Although not a traditional Indian spice, allspice features in the cuisine of the Near and Middle East. For best results buy the spice whole and grind in a mill or a pestle and mortar as needed.

HABITAT Native to the West Indies, especially Jamaica, Central America and Mexico. Now grown commercially in many tropical countries including Indonesia. Prefers hilly areas on limestone soils. In temperate northern zones the tree can be grown under glass but will not flower.

DESCRIPTION Evergreen tree resembling the myrtle, to 12m(40ft) with large, leathery, glossy green leaves 12.5cm(5in) long and prominently veined on the underside. Tree bears fruit after three years and small white flowers appear from June to August. These are followed by bunches of green berries that ripen to dark brown and look like large peppercorns.

Almond

Prunus dulcis, Prunus amygdalus

Rosaceae
Sweet almond

The almond has been cultivated in the Middle East for centuries and is mentioned in the Bible: Aaron's rod was an almond branch. According to Greek mythology, the almond was originally a grieving nymph, Phyllis, who had been deserted by her lover, Demophoon, and died of a broken heart. The gods took pity on her and changed her into a tree that burst into flower when Demophoon finally returned. The Greeks introduced the tree to Europe, and in the Middle Ages the nuts were an important article of commerce. In Elizabethan times quantities of almonds were pounded up with water to make a milky liquid that was used extensively in cooking. Today, cooling almond milk is still drunk as a kidney tonic and to ease heartburn. In culinary terms, the nuts are an important ingredient of Near and Middle Eastern dishes. In European cookery almonds are served with fish and made into a wide range of sweets such as *turron*, delicious Spanish nougat from Alicante.

Almonds yield around half their weight in an oil that is almost scentless and has excellent softening and nourishing properties. It keeps well and makes an excellent massage oil either on its own, or used as a carrier oil for selected essential oils in aromatherapy. Almond oil is light, easily absorbed by the skin and can help to alleviate itching eczema. Taken internally, it acts as a laxative. Ground almonds are also beneficial to the skin and make an excellent facial scrub that cleanses and softens.

The Bitter Almond, *Prunus amara*, is also widely cultivated for its oil and is used cosmetically and for massage. For almond essence and almond flavouring, bitter almonds are preferred.

HABITAT Native to the eastern Mediterranean, especially Jordan, Iran and the Middle East. Introduced to southern Europe and widely cultivated in all countries bordering on the Mediterranean, particularly Spain and Italy, as well as California. Prefers sun and well-drained soil.

DESCRIPTION Spreading tree to 7m(20ft) with smooth, pale-coloured branches. In common with other trees in this family, the cherry, peach and plum, pink or white blossom appears before the first leaves from mid to late spring. The flowers are solitary and stalkless and the leaves oval, pointed at the end and finely toothed. Fruit is dull green with an outer covering that toughens when ripe, then splits to reveal the familiar nuts in their yellowish, pitted shells.

Aloe

Aloe vera

Liliaceae

Barbados aloes, Curaçao aloes

Aloe vera, or the true aloe, was referred to in Greek writings as early as the fourth century BC. Most supplies came from the island of Socotra off the Horn of Africa, until the seventeenth century when aloes were exported to Europe from the West Indian islands of Curaçao and Barbados. To the ancient Greeks, aloe was a valuable purgative and they apparently attempted to conquer Socotra to procure specimens of the plant. Taken internally, aloe has a laxative action but causes griping pains, and it is now most commonly employed externally as a burn remedy. The fresh leaves exude a gelatinous juice that has remarkable healing properties when applied to damaged or irritated skin. Fresh aloe gel rapidly relieves burns, sunburn, dermatitis, eczema and poison-ivy rash. In the USA, *Aloe vera* has become an indispensable domestic first-aid plant since it is easily grown indoors as a houseplant. For minor burns or skin rashes, simply break off a leaf and apply the soothing juice to the affected part. In folk medicine, *Aloe vera* has acquired a reputation as an effective treatment for skin cancer, while studies have shown its effectiveness in treating radiation burns.

Cosmetically, *Aloe vera* gel was valued by the ancient Egyptian queen, Cleopatra, who massaged it into her skin. Aloe was also reputed to be the basis of the Empress Josephine's complexion milk. In recent years, this time-honoured cosmetic has enjoyed a revival and aloe gel is the main ingredient of many bodycare preparations, from moisturizing skin creams to suntan lotions.

HABITAT Found wild in eastern and southern Africa. Naturalized in North Africa, the Caribbean, and parts of the Mediterranean. Widely cultivated in the West Indies, Africa, Texas and Florida. Prefers stony, well-drained soil and a dry, sunny climate. Commonly grown as a houseplant.

DESCRIPTION Succulent perennial plant belonging to the lily family, from 30–150cm(1–5ft). The base of the plant is a rosette of fleshy, narrow, lance-shaped leaves 30–60cm(1–2ft) in length, with prickly edges and whitish-green on both sides. Clusters of yellow or orange-red flowers grow at the end of long stalks rising from the rosette and appear throughout most of the year. The stems may be woody.

GROWING TIPS Aloe needs a minimum temperature of 41°F(5°C) and a sunny position. It grows well in warm, dry rooms and requires little water. Propagate from off-shoots planted in gritty soil or make up a mixture of two parts soil to one part sand.

Amaranth

Amaranthus hypocondriacus

Amaranthaceae

Love-lies-bleeding, lady bleeding, prince's feather

Amaranth's flowers retain their shape and colour when dried, and Amaranth flower motifs were carved on ancient Greek tombs to symbolize immortality. On account of its blood-red flowers, amaranth was used to stop bleeding. The herb acts as an astringent and has been employed to treat diarrhoea, mouth ulcers and excessive menstrual flow.

HABITAT Native to the tropics and central American states. Found wild on both waste ground and cultivated land. Grown horticulturally.

DESCRIPTION Tall annual herb with a stout, erect, branched stem from 1–1.5m(3–5ft). The leaves are dull green with purple-red spots. Deeply veined on the underside, they are oval and taper to a point. Dense clusters of small, crimson to blood-red flowers appear in long, upright spikes in late summer.

American Cranesbill

Geranium maculatum

Geraniaceae

Wild geranium, spotted cranesbill

The botanical name *Geranium* refers to the beaked seeds of the plant, that were likened to the bill of the crane. The root has a diuretic action that is useful for diarrhoea, sore throats, and to stop bleeding.

HABITAT Native to eastern North America. Found wild in woodlands and on low ground as far north as Newfoundland.

DESCRIPTION Erect hairy plant to 60cm(2ft), with long-stalked leaves divided into five lobes and deeply incised. The leaves are coarsely toothed and become spotted with age. Large flowers with pale to rose-purple petals, veined at the base, grow in pairs from late spring to late summer followed by beaked seed capsules. The root is stout, brown externally and white inside.

Angelica
Angelica archangelica

Umbelliferae
Garden angelica, european angelica

Angelica has long been esteemed as a benevolent herb. According to fifteenth-century folklore, the plant had the power to ward off evil spirits and keep out witches, hence the practice of wearing necklaces of the leaves and making a holy water with the roots. Historically, angelica was deemed a protector of the body as well as the spirit. The herb acquired a reputation as a repellant of infectious disease and was employed during the Great Plague that swept over Europe in the mid-seventeenth century. According to Christian legend, angelica's protective powers were revealed by an angel to a dreaming monk. The plant was also said to come into bloom on the day of Michael the Archangel, hence the Latin name *archangelica*.

Angelica is a culinary herb of long standing. Its green stems are still candied – preserved in a sugar syrup – and used to decorate cakes and confectionery. The stems may also be added to stewed rhubarb or rhubarb jam. Both stems, and particularly the aromatic seeds, have been an important flavouring of liqueurs and cordials since the Middle Ages. Angelica is a principal ingredient of both Benedictine and Chartreuse liqueurs and is used in some vermouths. Angelica stems may be steamed and eaten with butter, like asparagus, while some enjoy adding the leaves to soups and green salads. An extract of the roots was once used to flavour tobacco.

Medicinally, angelica root and leaves have digestive properties and ease flatulence. Angelica is also warming and therefore beneficial for poor circulation. Angelica root has expectorant properties and is a traditional European and Native American Indian remedy for bronchial infections.

HABITAT Originated in Asia or northern Europe. Grows wild in cooler northern European countries as a garden escape and quickly establishes itself in damp meadows, on riverbanks and river islands. May also be found on waste ground. Cultivated for culinary purposes.

DESCRIPTION Tall, celery-like biennial or perennial herb to 2m(6ft). The stem is stout, hollow, and fluted, purplish at the base and branching near the top. The broad, bright green leaves are sheathed at the base, pinnate in form, deeply indented and subdivided. Small flowers, greenish-white and sweet smelling, grow in large, round umbels from mid-summer to early autumn. They are succeeded by aromatic pale yellow seeds.

GROWING TIPS Use fresh seed and sow as soon as ripe in a rich, damp soil. Thin the seedlings to 1m(3ft) apart. Prefers a combination of sun and shade, thriving best in a damp spot.

Aniseed

Pimpinella anisum

Umbelliferae

Anise

Cultivated by the ancient Egyptians, Greeks and Romans, aniseed was introduced to central Europe during the Middle Ages. The plant appeared in Britain from the mid-sixteenth century but the seed ripened successfully only during very warm summers. The Latin name *Pimpinella*, derived from *dipinella*, meaning bi-pinnate, refers to the form of the leaflets. They are arranged on either side of the leaf axis in the same way as a feather, with secondary leaflets similarly arranged.

In Roman times anise was grown in Tuscany for culinary and digestive purposes. The seeds contain a volatile oil that aids the digestion of rich foods, and were an important ingredient of a spiced cake, *mustaceum*, eaten by the Romans as a digestive dessert at the end of an elaborate feast. The origins of our traditional wedding cake may lie in this old Roman custom. A similar practice persists in many regional Indian cuisines, such as the Bengali, where aniseed, together with fennel, is the main ingredient of *paan*. Chewed after a spicy meal, this seed mixture prevents flatulence and sweetens the breath. Aniseed has long been used to flavour cakes and bread in eastern Europe and to make confectionery. In culinary terms, however, it is principally employed in spirits and liqueurs. In France the aniseed-based drinks *Anisette*, *Pastis*, *Ricard*, and *Pernod*, are particularly popular. The Greek version is *Ouzo*.

Medicinally, aniseed relieves flatulence and colic as well as improving the appetite. Aniseed was first prescribed for coughs by Hippocrates in the fifth century BC and herbalists still value its mild expectorant and antibiotic action in the treatment of bronchitis and tight, irritable coughs. The seeds were formerly an ingredient of powders for asthma, and used in cough mixtures and lozenges in combination with liquorice.

Star anise, *Illicium verum*, is the small star-shaped fruit of a native Chinese tree. An ingredient of Chinese Five Spice powder, it contains the same essential oil as anise and possesses similar properties. The flavour is stronger.

HABITAT Native of Egypt, Greece and the eastern Mediterranean, Grows on dry, poor soils in sunny situations. Widely cultivated in many warm climates, particularly the southern Mediterranean, North Africa, India, Turkey, and parts of South America.

DESCRIPTION Aromatic annual with erect stems to 60cm(2ft). The long-stalked, bright green leaves, like coriander, are lobed and kidney shaped at the base of the plant, becoming feathery and finely incised further up the stem. Numerous dainty white to yellowish-white flowers grow in sparse umbels during July and August followed by oval, hairy, brown, ribbed seeds. The seeds have a sweet taste.

Arnica

Arnica montana

Compositae

Leopard's bane, mountain tobacco, mountain daisy

Arnica has long been valued as a folk remedy for bruises and sprains, especially in mountainous areas of Europe where the incidence of such injuries is common. The plant is said to grow on the lower slopes of mountains, conveniently within reach of those who have fallen from the peaks. Applied externally, arnica ointment reduces inflammation and is particularly valued in Germany, where it is an ingredient of many medicinal preparations for external use. Arnica flowers may, however, cause dermatitis in people with very sensitive skin. This plant is perhaps the best known of all the homeopathic preparations, and widely used in the forms of pills, creams and tinctures. Both homeopaths and herbalists agree that arnica must not be used where the skin is broken. Internally, arnica can irritate the digestive system and is potentially toxic although it is considered safe in the minute doses required for homeopathic remedies. Homeopaths consider arnica a first-aid remedy and recommend it for bruising and to lessen the shock resulting from any injury. In homeopathic dosage too, arnica has a remarkable ability to stimulate the body's own healing powers and is valuable in aiding recovery after childbirth, surgery and tooth extractions.

Dried arnica leaves were once smoked as a tobacco substitute, hence the common name, mountain tobacco. The origin of arnica's other common name, leopard's bane, is uncertain.

HABITAT Grows wild in the mountain pastures and woodlands of central Europe and Siberia at altitudes of 1200–2800m(4000–9000ft). Naturalized in North America, and related species are found in Canada and the western part of the USA. Prefers sandy or loamy soils in sunny situations. Protected and cultivated in parts of central Europe for use in homeopathic preparations.

DESCRIPTION Aromatic perennial with a flat rosette of oval, downy, toothed, bright green leaves that rests on the ground. The stem is 30–60cm(1–2ft), hairy, with one to two pairs of smaller, opposite, leaves without stalks. Daisy-like yellow-orange flowers that are pleasantly scented appear from mid- to late summer. The petals are covered with fine, silky hairs and are notched at the tip.

GROWING TIPS Sow indoors or in a cold frame in a peaty or loamy soil mixed with sand in early spring. Plant out in a sunny, sheltered position in late spring.

Arrowroot

Maranta arundinaceae

Marantaceae

Maranta starch, Indian arrowroot

In Jamaica, mashed arrow root was made into a poultice for poisonous stings and arrow wounds. Medicinally, arrowroot soothes the digestive tract and hospitals formerly employed it in barium meals given prior to X-raying the gastro-intestinal system.

HABITAT Native to the West Indies and tropical America, from Mexico south to Brazil. Introduced to south-east Asia, India, and Africa and cultivated commercially on a small scale.

DESCRIPTION Perennial on a creeping rhizome with scaly, fleshy tubers. The stems are reed-like and grow to 2m(6ft) with smooth, oval leaves, sheathed at the base. Pairs of cream-coloured flowers appear at the ends of the long stems.

Artichoke

Cynara scolymus

Compositae

Globe artichoke

The artichoke is a vegetable delicacy and a valuable medicinal plant. The leaves and root have been prized since Medieval times for their beneficial effect on sluggish livers, and are also considered helpful for kidney problems and arteriosclerosis.

HABITAT Native to North Africa and found in sub-tropical and temperate zones such as the Canary Islands and southern Mediterranean countries. Cultivated commercially and found wild only as an escape from cultivation. Prefers rich, moist soils.

DESCRIPTION Thistle-like perennial with stems from 1–2m(3–6ft). Alternate, large leaves that rarely have prickles are greyish-green above and white and woolly beneath. The familiar, large, globular flower heads have spiny purple-green scales and purple thistle-like flowers that appear from late spring to mid summer.

Asparagus
Asparagus officinalis

Liliaceae
Garden asparagus, sparrow grass

Asparagus has been cultivated as a delicacy for over 2000 years. Medicinally, asparagus stimulates the filtering cells in the kidneys, increasing the flow of urine and giving it a pleasant scent.

HABITAT Found wild from the UK to central Asia on coasts and sandy areas, in woods and hedgerows. Extensively cultivated.

DESCRIPTION Perennial on short rootstock with edible greenish-pink fleshy shoots, that on maturing reach 1–3m (3–9ft). They bear needle-like leaves that are in fact branches: the leaves are scaly and inconspicuous. Small greenish-white, bell-shaped flowers appear in late spring and early summer, followed by a small red berry.

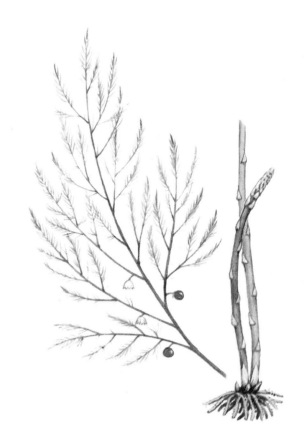

Avens
Geum urbanum

Rosaceae
Herb Bennet, wood avens

In Medieval times the aromatic root of avens, the blessed herb, was indispensable in the home for driving away evil spirits, repelling moths, and flavouring ale. Herbalists since Paracelsus have used avens to treat digestive disorders, and its astringency is considered helpful for diarrhoea.

HABITAT Native to Europe and common also in Russia and central Asia. Widespread in hedgerows, mixed woodland, and wood edges on moist soil.

DESCRIPTION Perennial with branched, slender, downy stems, to 30cm(12in). The larger, stalked, deep-green basal leaves are three lobed with toothed edges, and the smaller, upper leaves are stalkless. Solitary yellow flowers with five petals appear from late spring to early autumn followed by distinctive fruiting heads that terminate in a hook. The tough, fibrous root is 3–7cm(1–3in) long and smells of cloves.

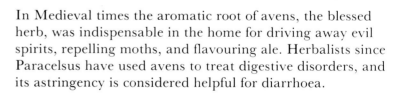

Balm

Melissa officinalis

Labiatae

Lemon balm, common balm

Melissa, the botanical name of this herb, is derived from the Greek for bee, and balm has been a popular bee plant in the Mediterranean for over 2000 years. According to Pliny writing in the first century: 'Bees are delighted with this plant above all others . . . when they are strayed away they do find their way home again by it'. It was said that bees would never leave a garden where balm grew, and when new bees were introduced to a hive, it was customary to rub the inside with balm to encourage them to stay.

Balm was a favourite remedy of the great eleventh-century Arabic physician Avicenna who regarded it as a heart tonic and uplifting to the spirits. The plant's reputation as a kind of herbal antidepressant continued into the seventeenth century when Culpeper declared that it 'driveth away all troublesome cares and thoughts out of the mind, arising from melancholy and black choler'. Modern tests on laboratory animals have confirmed balm's soothing effect by revealing that it acts as a sedative on the central nervous system, and present-day aromatherapists recommend the essential oil for depression, anxiety, nervous headaches and restlessness. Balm tea promotes sweating and is a traditional remedy for feverish colds; taken after food, balm tea also acts as a digestive. Since the volatile oils that are responsible for balm's therapeutic effects tend to evaporate on drying, herbalists recommend using the fresh plant.

In the kitchen, balm's lemon-flavoured leaves give a lemon tang to white wine cups, teas and fruit jellies. In Spain, they are added to sauces and salads. The fresh leaf may also be mixed with Indian tea for a refreshing drink.

HABITAT Native to southern and central Europe, North Africa and western Asia. Introduced and widespread in northern temperate zones, and often found wild as an escape. Naturalized in the south of England. Cultivated commercially as a garden plant. Prefers rich, moist soil and a sunny position.

DESCRIPTION Perennial similar to a bushy mint and very sweet smelling. Stems square and slightly hairy, from 30–80cm(12–32in), branched at the top and sometimes straggly. The greenish-yellow leaves are oval to heart-shaped at the base, coarsely serrate, and give off a sweet lemon scent when bruised. Small clusters of flowers appear in the axils from late summer to mid autumn, yellowish at first but often changing to pale pink or white.

Balm of Gilead

Commiphora opobalsamum

Burseraceae

Balsam of Gilead, balsam tree

The genuine Balm of Gilead, highly esteemed by the ancient Arabs, Egyptians, Turks, Greeks, and Romans was extracted from this small tree. At one time the sweet-scented resin was so highly prized that guards watched over trees cultivated in the gardens near Cairo. The herb's popular name is derived from the Greek *balsamon*, meaning a fragrant oil, while Gilead refers to its ancient cultivation on Mount Gilead in Israel. There are biblical references to the Balm of Gilead in Genesis and Jeremiah, and the Queen of Sheba is said to have presented a tree to Solomon as a gift.

The raw resin from this tree is thick, whitish and strongly perfumed. It solidifies on exposure to the air but is soluble in alcohol. Balm of Gilead was valued for its scent and once used as a beauty aid by ladies of the royal courts. It was also prescribed for diseases of the urinary tract. Today, true Balm of Gilead is scarce and supplies are likely to come from related North American trees, *Populus candicans* (illustrated) or *P. balsamifera*. These members of the poplar family took the name of their biblical counterpart on account of the sticky, heavily scented resin that covers the young buds. The major constituent of the resin is a group of aspirin-like compounds, or salicylates, that relieve pain and inflammation, while the oil content has an antiseptic and expectorant action. Herbalists recommend tincture of Balm of Gilead for sore throats, laryngitis and bronchitis. Externally, in the form of an ointment, the salicylates in Balm of Gilead are said to offer relief from the pain and inflammation caused by rheumatism and arthritis. These pain-relieving substances are also present in the bark of the American poplars and were once taken as a quinine substitute to bring down temperature in fevers.

HABITAT Cultivated in the countries bordering on the Red Sea – Saudi Arabia, Egypt, Sudan and Ethiopia. Introduced to Italy. Rare and difficult to grow.

DESCRIPTION Small tree to 4m(12ft) with spreading branches like wands and reddish-brown bark. The leaves are divided into groups of three, small and sparse. Small reddish flowers are followed by pea-sized reddish-grey berries. In summer the tree exudes a sweet-smelling resinous juice.

Balmony

Chelone glabra

Scrophulariaceae

Turtlebloom, Turtlehead

Balmony takes its botanical name from the Greek for tortoise, and the flowers resemble a turtle's head. Native Americans took the bitter-tasting leaves for their laxative properties, and the herb was a traditional remedy for worms. Today herbalists value balmony for its tonic action on the liver.

HABITAT Native to North America from Newfoundland, south to Florida and west to Texas. Found on low-lying marshy ground, in damp thickets, and on stream and river banks.

DESCRIPTION Beautiful perennial with an erect, square stem, 60cm(2ft) to 120cm(4ft). The opposite, shiny leaves are narrow with serrated edges and taper to a point. Short dense spikes of two-lipped, scentless, white flowers tinged with pink apper from July to September.

Barberry

Berberis vulgaris

Berberidaceae

European barberry, pepperidge bush

For Native American Indians, barberry-bark tea was taken for its restorative effect after illness. The root has laxative properties and the soothing astringency of the berries relieves sore throats. The sweetened berries are popular in jams and preserves.

HABITAT Native to Europe and eastwards to eastern Asia. Naturalized in north-eastern USA from Nova Scotia south to Pennsylvania and westwards to Iowa in light woodland and hedgerows. Now scarce in the wild.

DESCRIPTION Deciduous, branched shrub to 2m(7ft), with greyish, woody stems and three sharp spines at the branch nodes. The pale green, glossy leaves are spoon shaped with fine, sharp teeth. Small, bright yellow flowers hang from the branches in clusters from mid-spring, followed by orange-red oblong berries.

Basil

Ocimum basilicum

Labiatae

Sweet basil, garden basil

Basil was introduced to Europe from India, where a related species, *Ocimum sanctum*, is sacred to the Hindu gods Vishnu and Krishna. It was once customary in Hindu homes to place a sprig of basil on the dead before burial, to ensure their safe passage to the next world. According to medieval superstition, scorpions liked to hide beneath pots of basil, and a sprig left under the pot would hatch into a scorpion. In a story from Bocaccio's *Decameron*, adapted by Keats into 'Isabella or the Pot of Basil', a woman keeps her murdered lover's head in a pot of basil and waters it with her tears. Basil continued to inspire fear well into the seventeenth century, when it was popularly believed that taking snuff made from the powdered leaves, or even smelling it, would allow scorpions to nest in your brain. One explanation for basil's deadly reputation is a confusion of its Latin name *basilicus* with basilisk – a fabulous reptile with a fatal glance that struck dead anyone crossing its path.

Basil's principal use is culinary. The pungent fresh leaves are the principal ingredient of the classic Italian pasta sauce, *pesto Genovese*, and basil's flavour is particularly compatible with tomatoes. Indeed the two are companion plants. The sweet, faintly clove-like taste of fresh basil is lost on drying and purists avoid the dried herb at all costs. A pot of fresh basil is particularly useful in the kitchen since it repels flies, and apparently it was once common to find pots on the tables of pavement cafes in southern France.

Basil is no longer employed medicinally, although herbalists consider the herb both sedative and digestive. Hot basil tea is said to be helpful in alleviating indigestion and stomach cramps. The dried, powdered herb was once taken as snuff to clear the head in cases of headache or colds.

HABITAT Native to India; also southern Asia and the Middle East. Cultivated extensively in southern, central and eastern Europe, North Africa, and also in the USA, particularly California.

DESCRIPTION Very aromatic, bushy annual from 30–60cm (1–2ft) with branching stems that bear tender, light green, oval leaves with slightly toothed margins. Clusters of small, white, two-lipped flowers appear towards the tops of the stems from mid- to late summer. One hybrid has purple-tinged leaves and pink flowers.

GROWING TIPS Sow seed indoors in late spring and plant outside in early summer, or when the soil has warmed. Plant out in rich, well-drained soil in a sunny, sheltered position. Mist the leaves and water frequently in hot weather.

Bay

Laurus nobilis

Lauraceae

Sweet bay, sweet laurel

According to Greek myth, the sun-god Apollo tried to force his attentions on a beautiful nymph, Daphne. In a desperate attempt to escape she called upon Gaia, the Earth Mother, who opened up the ground and caused a bay tree to spring up in her place. Apollo claimed the bay as his sacred tree and wore a crown of its leaves, a practice later adopted to glorify emperors, athletes, victors and scholars. Apollo was also the god of music and poetry, and poets were honoured with laurel, a custom that still persists in the British tradition of appointing a Poet Laureate – a poet crowned with laurel. The glorious bay tree was also endowed with protective properties: according to a superstition that was still prevalent in Culpeper's day, standing under a bay tree would shield you from thunder, lightening and witches. When a bay tree died, it was considered an ill omen.

Bay's medicinal application evolved naturally from its protective powers and the leaves were put to a wide range of uses, including inducing abortions and curing snakebites, urinary problems and rheumatism. Today, herbalists still consider bay-leaf oil an effective rub for stiff or rheumatic joints, and a bay-leaf infusion may ease indigestion and flatulence. Bay's principal use, however, is in the kitchen. It is virtually indispensable in French and Mediterranean cooking, and is one of the ingredients of *bouquet garni*, the classic French seasoning. Bay leaves improve the flavour of sauces, and can be added to the water when cooking rice or pulses. Dried bay leaves are traditionally placed in flour bins to deter weevils. Bay is usually used dried, as the strong flavour of fresh leaves can be bitter and overpower other flavours in a dish.

HABITAT Probably originated in Asia Minor and well-established in the Mediterranean. Grows wild in high, sheltered, sunny valleys with rich soil. European variety usually grown as a bush. Widely cultivated commercially in the Mediterranean, North Africa, Temperate regions of the USA and central America.

DESCRIPTION Evergreen tree with shiny, grey bark that may grow to over 14m(45ft) in ideal conditions but is usually restricted to 2m(6ft). The glossy, dark green, leathery leaves are aromatic when crushed, oval in shape and pointed at both ends. From late spring to early autumn clusters of small yellow-white flowers appear in the leaf axils, followed by dark purple berries resembling small olives.

GROWING TIPS Propagation from cuttings is difficult and rooting may take up to nine months. Young nursery trees can be planted directly in the garden, or in tubs with rich soil, plus sand. Choose a sunny, sheltered position, and protect from frost.

Bayberry

Myrica cerifera

Myricaceae

Wax myrtle, candleberry

Bayberry furnishes a scented wax that American settlers made into candles and soap. The dried root bark has astringent properties and is a traditional remedy for sore throats and diarrhoea.

HABITAT Native to the eastern states of the USA, from New Jersey, south to Florida and Texas. Found on sandy soils around coastal marshes, on stream banks, and in meadows.

DESCRIPTION An evergreen shrub or a small tree to 11m(35ft), much branched and covered with smooth, grey bark. The leaves are lance shaped and shine with fragrant, resinous glands. In spring yellowish, catkin-like flowers appear, followed by groups of greyish- or greenish-white crusty, waxen berries.

Bearberry

Arctostaphylos uva-ursi

Ericaceae

Bears' grape, mountain box

Bearberry is a powerful astringent and antiseptic that has long been used to treat bladder infections and kidney stones. Applied externally, a wash of bearberry leaves is a folk remedy for halting the spread of poison ivy rash. The berries are tasteless, except perhaps to bears.

HABITAT Found in cooler climates, such as northern Europe and northern USA as far south as northern California. Prefers moors and coniferous woodland with rocky or sandy soils. Cultivated as an ornamental.

DESCRIPTION Low, trailing evergreen shrub to 15cm(6in) that has many branches covered with dark flaky bark. The leathery, dark green leaves form thick mats and are rounded at the apex. Drooping stems of bell-shaped white, pink or reddish-tinged flowers similar to heather are followed in autumn by bright red, currant-sized, shining berries.

Belladonna

Atropa belladonna

Solanaceae

Deadly nightshade, dwale, devil's berries

This exceptionally poisonous plant plants owes its botanical name to Atropos, one of the three Fates in Greek mythology. While her sisters Clotho and Lachesis weave and measure the thread of human life, Atropos cuts it at the appointed time. *Belladonna* is probably named in honour of the Italian ladies who made eyedrops of the fresh juice to dilate their pupils and make them appear more alluring. According to medieval superstition, witches used belladonna in their ceremonies to promote hallucinations, and it was combined with aconite to produce the sensation of flying. Gerard described the herb as 'a plant so furious and deadly: for it bringeth such as have eaten thereof into a dead sleepe wherein many have died'. Indeed, in 1582, the King of Scotland's soldiers are reputed to have prepared a belladonna brew strong enough to knock out an entire Danish army who were then murdered in their beds.

Belladonna has powerful sedative and narcotic properties, mainly due to the presence of two poisonous crystalline alkaloids, atropine and hyoscyamine, that affect the autonomic nervous system. Today, opthalmologists still use atropine to dilate the pupils, and it also antidotes the nerve gas discharged by chemical weapons. The other alkaloid, hyoscyamine, is used as a sedative. Belladonna extract is used medicinally to treat ailments characterized by spasms, including Parkinson's disease, epilepsy, asthma and whooping cough. Atropine also controls mucous secretions and may be found in medications for colds and hayfever. Homeopathically, belladonna is prescribed for fevers, scarlet fever, inflammations, throbbing headaches and sore throats.

CAUTION   All parts of the plant are highly poisonous. Do not handle and take only under medical supervision.

HABITAT Native to Europe and south-western Asia; naturalized in the eastern states of the USA. Grows on wasteland, in quarries, ruins and on wooded hills. Prefers some shade, and chalk or limestone soils.

DESCRIPTION Perennial with stout, branched, purplish stem, to 1.25m(5ft) on a thick, fleshy rootstock. All parts of the fresh plant give off an unpleasant smell when bruised and are extremely poisonous. The stem divides higher up into three to four branches with dull-green, veined, oval leaves that are pointed at the apex and in pairs of unequal sizes. Dingy purple, furrowed, bell-shaped flowers tinged with green appear from mid to late summer. They are succeeded by very shiny, black berries the size of a small cherry. They contain a sweet, inky juice that is a deadly poison.

Bergamot

Monarda didyma

Labiatae

Bee balm, Oswego tea, red bergamot

The *Monarda* or horsemint genus takes its name from a sixteenth-century Spanish herbalist, Nicholas de Monardes, who learned of its medicinal properties from Native American Indians. The plant is called bergamot because its scent is reminiscent of the bergamot orange. It is the oil of that orange, and not this plant, that is used to perfume and flavour the popular British tea, Earl Grey. Bergamot, however, has been drunk as a tea in its own right, hence its common name Oswego tea. Oswego, or more properly Otsego, is the old name for a tribe that lived in an area of what is now New York, and where bergamot grew abundantly. Its leaves were used for a popular tea after the Boston Tea Party in 1773, a protest at the tax imposed by the British on Indian tea. In many American homes, and in Shaker settlements, bergamot was drunk as a substitute for expensive Indian tea.

Native American Indians have long used both red and purple bergamot medicinally to treat mild fevers, headaches, colds and sore throats. Some tribes inhaled the oil for catarrhal conditions while others applied a poultice of the leaves to boils and spots. Today herbalists prescribe bergamot tea for nausea, flatulence, menstrual cramps and vomiting. An inhalation is beneficial for colds and sore throats. The plant contains a volatile oil that was once used in perfumery and hair products.

HABITAT Native to North America in rich, moist soils from Maine west to Michigan and Ontario, and south to Georgia. Naturalized in South America. Prefers part shade and grows wild in moist deciduous woods and thickets. Widely cultivated horticulturally as a border plant for its scarlet flowers.

DESCRIPTION Aromatic perennial with square, hairy, erect stem to 1m(3ft). The leaves are fairly rough, oval and deep green. They are arranged in pairs and have serrated edges. In some cultivated varieties the leaves are mint-scented. From mid-summer to early autumn very attractive tufted, scarlet flowers with two lips grow in whorls at the top of the stem. The whole plant smells pleasantly of orange, and so makes a fragrant addition to any garden.

GROWING TIPS An excellent border plant. Propagate from seed sown in spring or by root division. Seedlings take about a year to establish themselves and will grow well in ordinary, preferably light garden soil. Choose a sunny position, but with some shade. Some gardeners advise digging up the roots after three years' flowering and replanting only the outer suckers.

Bethroot

Trillium erectum

Liliaceae

Brown Beth, squawroot

Bethroot is a traditional Appalachian Indian remedy for treating disorders of the female reproductive system. The root has astringent properties useful for stemming the flow of blood in post-partum haemorrhage, while its steroid-like principles help to regulate the menstrual cycle.

HABITAT Native to North America from Quebec to North Carolina. Found wild in shady woods on rich, moist soils.

DESCRIPTION Perennial to 50cm(20in) with a short, thick root, rust-coloured externally and pale yellow inside. The broad, veined, stalkless leaves are almost square and taper to a point. They are grouped in threes in whorls at the end of the stem. In late spring, a small nodding, three-petalled white to brownish purple flower appears at the stem tip.

Betony

Stachys officinalis, Betonica officinalis

Labiatae

Wood betony, bishopswort

The ancient Egyptians endowed betony with magical powers and the Romans maintained that it would cure 40 different ailments. Betony, a traditional headache cure, possesses mild sedative and relaxant properties that herbalists consider helpful in alleviating tense, nervous headaches and neuralgia.

HABITAT European native widely distributed in the UK but rare in Scotland. Found on light, sandy soils in open woodland, along wooded paths, in copses and meadowland.

DESCRIPTION Nettle-like perennial to 50cm(20in) with a square, grooved stem and a rosette of long-stalked, large basal leaves. The roughish upper leaves are stalkless, dotted with glands, and the margins have rounded teeth. From mid-summer to mid-autumn terminal spikes of two-lipped purplish-red flowers appear.

Birch

Betula alba and *Betula pendula*

Betulaceae
White birch, paper birch, silver birch

Rolls of birch bark found in Mesolithic excavations served as paper, and Native Americans used it to build canoes. Herbalists consider birch-leaf tea a cleansing diuretic and recommend it for urinary gravel, fluid retention and cystitis. Native Americans drank black birch tea to relieve headaches.

HABITAT Widespread in northern and central Europe, the northern USA, and Canada. Grows in open woods, on heathland and on the lower slopes of mountains and valleys.

DESCRIPTION Graceful deciduous tree to 20m(65ft) with smooth, white, papery bark. The slender branches bear beech-like, triangular, bright green leaves with irregularly serrated margins. Pale green, hanging male catkins and smaller, more erect female catkins appear in spring.

Bistort

Polygonum bistorta

Polygonaceae
Snake root, easter ledge

In the north of England a pudding of fresh bistort leaves plus nettle tops and eggs was commonly eaten at Easter. Bistort is very astringent and is a traditional folk remedy for diarrhoea and dysentery.

HABITAT European native and widespread in the north of England. May be found west of the Rockies in North America. Grows on roadsides, in damp meadows, open woodland and on stream banks.

DESCRIPTION Perennial with a thick, black, twisted S-shaped root up to 1m(3ft) in length. Erect stem with swollen joints to 50cm(20in), with a few broad, dock-like leaves that taper to a point. The leaf stalks are crimson towards the base. Dense, conspicuous spikes of rose-pink or flesh-coloured flowers bloom from mid-summer to mid-autumn.

Blackberry

Rubus fructicosus

Rosaceae
Bramble

For thousands of years Europeans have been gathering blackberries from the wild for food. The rampant shrubs abound in both town and country and for many families 'blackberrying' is an enjoyable autumn ritual. The juicy berries make excellent jelly, pies, wine and vinegar. Blackberry jelly and wine were considered fine cordials from the late seventeenth century, especially with the addition of a little brandy. The fruit is rich in vitamin C and is a good source of dietary fibre. Country superstitions about the correct time for picking blackberries still persist. After his fall from grace, the Devil is said to have landed on a blackberry bush and to render the fruit unfit to eat once a particular date has passed. In the UK, blackberries must be gathered before Michaelmas, September 29. After this date the Devil contaminates the berries by spitting or urinating on them. Blackberries feature in the Bible and they were known to the ancient Greeks who considered them beneficial for gout.

A tea of blackberry leaves has long been valued as a home cure for sore throats and diarrhoea, while chewing the fresh leaves is an ancient remedy for bleeding gums. Crawling beneath bramble arches was once the traditional cure for boils in south-west England. Today, a simpler alternative is to drink a cleansing blackberry leaf tea or to make a poultice from fresh, lightly boiled leaves. Blackberry vinegar is a remedy of long standing for feverish colds.

HABITAT Native to Europe and found in north-eastern and central states of America. Common hedgerow plant and widespread on scrubland, thickets, and wood edges. Invasive in gardens and near habitation. Cultivated for its fruit.

DESCRIPTION Sprawling shrub with woody and densely prickled stems. The trailing, tenacious stems can extend to 5m(15ft) and root when in contact with the ground. The dark green leaves are grouped in threes or fives and are covered with fine hairs: the edges are serrated. White or pale pink flowers appear from mid-summer to mid-autumn followed by the familiar fleshy berries that ripen to black. Flowers and fruit may appear together on the same plant.

Blackcurrant

Ribes nigrum

Saxifragaceae

Quinsy berries

Wild blackcurrants were once widespread in the wooded areas of northern Europe and gathered for food. Today the fruit is extensively cultivated along with several other varieties including white and green currants. The wild berries have long been made into jams, jellies and pies; homemade blackcurrant brandy and blackcurrant wine were also popular. Today cultivated blackcurrants are widely used in the food and drinks industries. A particularly rich source of vitamin C, they are the main constituent of many cordials and drinks, some of them designed to appeal to children, thus ensuring that they receive an adequate supply of the vitamin. The French blackcurrant syrup *cassis* has become very popular in recent years. Added to chilled white wine, it makes a refreshing summer aperitif known as *kir*. Fresh blackcurrant leaves may also be steeped in white wine for added flavour, and a cold infusion of the leaves is considered very thirst-quenching in hot weather.

It was, however, for its medicinal properties that the blackcurrant was primarily valued. As quinsy berries, the plant's popular name, clearly indicates, blackcurrants were first used as a home remedy for inflamed sore throats. Quinsy is a form of tonsillitis. Indeed, blackcurrant throat lozenges are still widely available. Blackcurrant juice and blackcurrant-leaf tea were also used to treat whooping cough in children. The leaves are particularly cleansing and make an excellent gargle for bleeding gums as well as promoting good all-round oral hygiene. Blackcurrant leaves were once drunk as a tea substitute and are still included in herbal tea mixtures.

HABITAT Native to Europe, particularly northern and central regions, and western Asia. Naturalized in North America. Formerly found wild in moist soils, especially in the damp woods of northern Europe, and in the hilly UK counties of Yorkshire and Cumbria. Widely cultivated both horticulturally and commercially for its fruit.

DESCRIPTION Perennial shrub to 2m(6ft) with woody branches, lacking spines. The strongly perfumed leaves are dark green, dotted beneath, and borne on long stalks. Appearing in alternate pairs or in clusters, the leaves are divided into three or five rounded lobes with serrated margins. In spring, greenish-white flowers hang from the axils in clusters, followed by the familiar small, soft, dark purple berries.

Black Root

Veronicastrum virginicum, Leptandra virginica

Schrophulariaceae

Culver's root, bowman's root

Fresh black root is a powerful emetic and Native Americans employed it for medicinal and ritualistic purposes. Today, herbalists may prescribe small doses of the gentler dried root to relieve problems, such as jaundice, that are associated with liver congestion.

HABITAT Native to North America from New England to Kansas. Prefers moist woods and meadows, marshes and river banks.

DESCRIPTION Perennial to 2m(6ft) on a horizontal, blackish cylindrical rhizome. The stem is smooth, erect and unbranched and bears, at intervals, whorls of three to five lance-shaped leaves. Branching, terminal spikes of numerous white flowers appear from mid-summer to mid-autumn, followed by oblong seed capsules.

Bladderwrack

Fucus vesiculosus

Fucaceae

Kelp, sea-wrack

Bladderwrack, commonly known as kelp, is not only a traditional sea vegetable and fertilizer, but also a medicine. It is the original source of iodine, a valuable mineral essential to the healthy functioning of the thyroid gland. Herbalists also recommend bladderwrack compresses for easing inflamed rheumatic joints.

HABITAT Commonly found on the coastlines of western Scotland, Norway and the Atlantic coast of North America.

DESCRIPTION Strong-smelling, fan-shaped seaweed with a thin, leathery texture. The perennial frond is yellow to brownish-green in colour and 1m(3ft) long, and its woody stalk adheres to the rocks by means of a disc-shaped sucker. The stalk has a prominent mid-rib with pairs of air sacs running along its length. At the wavy tips, where the frond

divides, are spherical receptacles, which are filled with transparent mucus.

Blessed Thistle

Cnicus benedictus

Compositae

Sacred thistle, St Benedict thistle

Blessed thistle, once considered a cure-all, was also a popular vegetable: the root was eaten boiled and the heads cooked like artichokes. Today herbalists consider it an effective bitter tonic that stimulates the appetite and strengthens the digestive system.

HABITAT Mediterranean native. Introduced throughout Europe and occasionally found wild in North America. Generally found in waste places on stony ground.

DESCRIPTION Annual, downy, thistle-like plant with a bristly, branched stem to 70cm(27in). The long, narrow, lance-shaped leaves are dark green with distinctive white veins. The margins are wavy with irregular indentations that end in sharp prickles. From early summer to early autumn pale yellow flowers appear, set in prickly green heads and partially concealed by brown spines.

Blood Root

Sanguinaria canadensis

Papaveraceae

Indian paint, red pucoon

Native Americans used the orange-red juice of the fresh plant as a body paint and fabric dye. Herbalists may recommend small doses of blood root as an expectorant in cases of bronchitis but the therapeutic dosage is very small and large doses are toxic.

HABITAT Native to North America and common in New England. Also found westwards to Illinois and southwards to Tennessee. Grows on moist, rich soils in woods and on shaded slopes.

DESCRIPTION Perennial plant from 15–30cm(6–12in) on a thick rhizome with orange-red rootlets that send up a sheath leaf stalk. The leaf is deeply lobed, hand-shaped, and pale grey-green with toothed edges. From mid-spring to early summer a single, white, cup-shaped flower with golden stamens appears.

Blue Cohosh

Caulophyllum thalictroides

Berberidaceae

Papoose root, blue ginseng

Native American women took blue cohosh tea during the later stages of pregnancy to make labour shorter and less painful. Modern herbalists now consider the plant unsafe during pregnancy since it may overstimulate the uterus and result in miscarriage.

HABITAT Native to eastern North America, westwards to Manitoba and southwards to Tennessee. Found in moist woodland and near mountain streams.

DESCRIPTION Erect perennial to 1m(3ft) with a knotted, fragrant rootstock. The mature, bluish-green oval leaves are large, stalkless and divided into three, and often further divided into two or three lobes. Yellow-green to purple-brown flowers with six petals appear from late spring, followed by dark blue pea-sized berries.

Blue Flag

Iris versicolor

Iridaceae

Flag lily, liver lily

Blue flag is a traditional Native American remedy for gastric upsets. It acts on the liver, hence its common name, liver lily. Herbalists value the internal cleansing properties of the dried root and recommend it for eruptive skin complaints. The fresh root is poisonous.

HABITAT Native to central and eastern areas of North America, and introduced to Europe. Grows abundantly in swamps and bogs and prefers a peaty soil.

DESCRIPTION Perennial iris growing to 1m(3ft) from a thick, creeping, dark brown rhizome. The thick, coarse stem bears long, sword-shaped, pale green leaves and in early summer purple-blue or violet flowers, typical of irises, appear. There are white or white and yellow markings at the base of each petal, and the flowers are succeeded by leathery seed pods.

Bogbean
Menyanthes trifoliata

Menyanthaceae
Buckbean, marsh trefoil

Medicinally, bogbean has been used to treat a wide variety of ailments including gout and rheumatism, while its vitamin C content made it a useful remedy for scurvy. Bogbean's bitter principles act as a digestive tonic.

HABITAT Native to the northern hemisphere from the Pacific coast of N. America across Europe and Asia to Siberia. Grows in freshwater marshes, bogs and ditches on peaty soils.

DESCRIPTION Perennial water plant with a dense matting of roots. The thick stem, to 25cm(10in), is partly enveloped by the large, sheathing bases of the dark green leaves. These have a prominent pale mid-rib and three discrete, rounded lobes. From early summer distinctive, pinkish, five-petalled flowers covered with feathery white hairs appear.

Boneset
Eupatorium perfoliatum

Compositae
Feverwort

Boneset is a Native American remedy for feverish conditions that became popular among North American settlers. The name boneset was coined following the herb's success in alleviating a virulent strain of influenza known as 'break-bone fever', prevalent in nineteenth-century North America.

HABITAT Native to Mexico and naturalized in North America. Common in open marshland, swampy ground and along the banks of streams from Dakota south to Florida.

DESCRIPTION Perennial from 60cm–1.5m(2–5ft) on a thick, hairy, cylindrical stem. Branching above, the stem bears many lance-shaped, sharply pointed leaves with finely serrated edges. The dark green leaves are rough above and downy with resinous glands beneath. Short, dense flat-topped clusters of white flowers appear from late summer to mid-autumn. The whole plant is slightly aromatic.

Borage

Borago officinalis

Boraginaceae

Herb of gladness, burrage

Commonly known as herb of gladness, borage's powers of uplifting the spirits and dispelling gloom are referred to in all the historical writings on the herb. Pliny quotes an ancient Latin verse that translates as 'I, Borage, bring always gladness' and according to Gerard, 'the leaves and flowers of borage put in wine do make men and women glad and merry and drive away all sadness, dullness and melancholy'. Culpeper assigned the astrological ruleship of borage to Jupiter, planet of expansiveness and generosity, and put it under Leo, the sign that rules the heart. In herbal medicine today, borage's restorative action on the adrenal glands is thought to be responsible for its strengthening and stress-relieving properties. Modern herbalists respect borage's traditional uses and continue to recommend it for restoring lost vitality and flagging spirits, especially during convalescence. According to one recent account, borage leaves proved a very effective cure for a hangover and left the writer feeling remarkably cheerful and clear-headed. A particularly versatile herb, borage also promotes sweating and has expectorant properties, both of which are beneficial for feverish, chesty colds.

At one time, young borage leaves were eaten in salads, principally on account of their reputation for inducing a state of euphoria. Fortunately, they also have a pleasant cucumber-like smell and taste and may be added to cucumber soup and green salads, or chopped very finely and mixed with soft cheeses. The attractive blue flowers found their way into a wide variety of alcoholic drinks for their cordial effect, and are still added to summer wine cups, homemade lemonade, and cocktails. Borage flowers may also be crystallized, like rose petals or violets.

HABITAT Native to the Mediterannean region and naturalized throughout Europe and the UK. Cultivated commercially. Rarely found wild, except as an escape near habitation and and on rubbish dumps.

DESCRIPTION Hardy annual, sometimes biennial, with erect stems to 60cm(2ft). The whole plant is covered with rough white hairs and is very prickly to the touch. The stem bears large, alternate, deep-green leaves without stalks. They are oval in shape, veined, wrinkled, and pointed at the apex. From early summer to early autumn, striking bright blue star-shaped flowers with distinctive black anthers appear at the ends of the branched stems. The flowers are very attractive to bees.

GROWING TIPS Borage is self-seeding and very prolific. Sow seed in late spring in ordinary well-drained soil. Thin out and transplant to a sunny position.

Broom

Sarothamnus scoparius

Papilionaceae

Scotch broom, besom

In medieval Europe, broom was known as *Planta genista* and was adopted as a heraldic emblem by one of the Dukes of Brittany. Struck by its golden flowers and its habit of rooting firmly among the rocks, he wore a spray of the plant as he rode into battle and afterwards kept it as his crest. *Planta genista* became Plantagenet, the family name of the Duke's descendants from King Henry II to Richard III of England. Today, the Plantagenet emblem can still be seen in the broom pod motif that decorates the robe of Richard II's statue in Westminster Abbey. Sadly, the pods are open and empty, a symbol of Richard's defeat at the Battle of Pontefract.

In the home, broom has always been a most useful and versatile plant. As the name suggests, broom twigs were tied in bundles for sweeping floors centuries before the introduction of the brush. Witches, too, favoured these besoms, or broomsticks, but put them to a quite different use. In Scotland, where broom grows abundantly (hence the name Scotch broom), it was employed for thatching cottage roofs and fashioned into baskets and screens for the home. In the kitchen, broom buds were pickled and eaten like capers, the bitter young green tops added to ale, and the seeds roasted and ground as a coffee substitute. The bark contains tannin, used for tanning leather, while the fibrous part of the bark was once employed in paper and cloth manufacture.

Medicinally, young broom shoots have mild diuretic properties and are a traditional folk remedy for fluid retention. European herbalists still prescribe broom in cases of water retention due to a weak heart, often in conjunction with Lily of the Valley and Hawthorn. Many American herbalists, however, consider sparteine, an alkaloid present in the plant, unsafe.

CAUTION   Broom must be avoided by those suffering from high blood pressure.

HABITAT Native to the UK, common in central and southern Europe, northern Asia, and naturalized in the USA. Grows abundantly on heathland, and on the edges of woods and in woodland clearings. Prefers dry, sandy, acid soils.

DESCRIPTION Deciduous shrub to 1.5m(5ft). Bears many slender, wand-like, sparsely leaved branches similar to those of gorse but without prickles. The lower leaves have stalks and three oblong leaflets; the upper leaves are smaller and stalkless. Both sets of leaves are alternate and hairy when young. From early spring to mid-summer dense sprays of very fragrant, brilliant yellow, pea-shaped flowers appear. They are succeeded by flattened seed pods that become black on ripening and explode with a cracking sound.

Brooklime

Veronica beccabunga

Scrophulariaceae

Water pimpernel, cow cress

Brooklime is often found growing alongside watercress. It has a similar sharp but slightly more bitter taste and was traditionally eaten in salads and as a spring vegetable. Medicinally, brooklime was a fourteenth-century home remedy for gout and swellings, and was once prescribed for liver problems.

HABITAT Widespread in all parts of the UK, Europe, Asia, and North Africa. Found along the banks of streams, ditches and near freshwater ponds.

DESCRIPTION Semi-aquatic perennial with succulent, hollow, creeping stems that root at intervals and sometimes float in the water. The leaves are opposite, shiny green, and oblong with rounded ends. Thick and fleshy in texture, the leaves have slightly toothed margins. Numerous small, bright blue and white flowers on short stems flower during the whole of the summer months.

Buchu

Agathosma betulina

Rutaceae

Round buchu

Buchu is a traditional black South African herb that contains a fragrant, antiseptic oil. Steeped in oil, the leaves make a perfumed body rub, and a tea was drunk for digestive problems. Today herbalists recommend buchu for cystitis and bladder infections, unless the kidneys are weak.

HABITAT Indigenous to the Cape Province of South Africa. Grows wild on the dry soil of mountainsides and hillsides. Cultivated commercially.

DESCRIPTION Deciduous shrub to 1.5m(5ft). The smooth, straight branches bear glossy, pale green, leathery leaves. Oil glands are dotted throughout the leaves and give off a peppermint-like smell. The leaf tips are blunt, with a

pronounced curve, and the margins are finely toothed. The flowers are small with five petals.

Burdock

Arctium lappa

Compositae

Beggar's buttons, gypsy's rhubarb

Sweet-tasting burdock root was traditionally eaten boiled or roasted, and the young stems cooked like asparagus. In Japan it is still cultivated as a vegetable. Medicinally, burdock is well-established in European and Native American medicine as a blood purifier. Herbalists use it to treat such skin problems as acne and psoriasis.

HABITAT Widespread in the UK, Europe and northern USA. Grows on waste ground, along fences, and on roadsides.

DESCRIPTION Biennial with stout, dull green hairy stem to 1m(3ft) on a long, grey-brown vertical root. The large leaves are dock-like, with long reddish stalks and wavy margins. They are furrowed above, woolly beneath, and roughen with age. Small red or purple flowers that resemble thistles are set in distinctive fruiting heads covered with hooked burrs, appearing from late summer.

Camphor

Cinnamomum camphor

Lauraceae

Laurel camphor

Camphor oil was considered a valuable medicine as early as the twelfth century, and it is a traditional rub for easing painful, rheumatic joints. Camphor's penetrating odour repels moths and it was formerly the active ingredient in mothballs.

HABITAT Tree indigenous to China and Japan that flourishes in tropical and subtropical climates. Introduced in California and Florida.

DESCRIPTION Dense-topped evergreen to 12m(39ft), similar to the lime and much branched. The alternate, shiny leaves taper to a point and smell of camphor. Clusters of small white flowers appear in summer followed by a red berry, similar to cinnamon.

Caraway

Carum carvi

Umbelliferae

Caraway seed

Caraway derives its name from an ancient Arabic word meaning seed and has been valued both for its flavour and its medicinal properties since the time of the ancient Egyptians. Caraway seed has been found in Mesolithic excavations that date back 5000 years, and the Bible mentions its cultivation. In the Middle Ages the carrot-like root was boiled as a vegetable and the young chopped leaves added to soups and salads. Caraway-seed bread and cakes were commonly eaten in Elizabethan England and a caraway-seed cake was traditionally offered to farm labourers when they had finished sowing the wheat. Today many people consider caraway an acquired taste, except in Germany and Austria where it has retained its popularity. There, caraway seed flavours rye bread, cakes and cheese, and is an ingredient of sauerkraut and *kummel*, a traditional German liqueur. On a symbolic level, caraway was reputed to prevent departures: it was included in love potions to ensure fidelity, as well as being fed to fowl to prevent them straying.

Like many culinary herbs, caraway contains a volatile oil that has digestive properties. A traditional remedy for indigestion, especially where there is flatulence, caraway seeds were drunk as a tea, made into a cordial, and also taken in the form of digestive 'comfits' or sweets. It is also said that baked apples were served with caraway to make them more digestible. Herbalists continue to recommend caraway seed or oil for dyspepsia and for colic in children. Caraway seed stimulates a weak appetite while its anti-griping qualities are said to be beneficial for menstrual cramps.

HABITAT Widespread over northern and central Europe, temperate Asia, and the Middle East. Naturalized in the northern and northwestern USA. In the UK, most wild caraway is an escape from cultivation. Tolerates most soils and prefers waste ground. Grown on a commercial scale in Germany, Holland, and Russia.

DESCRIPTION Biennial on a slender, white taproot with hollow, ridged stems to 80cm(32in). The whole plant is pleasantly aromatic and has finely cut feathery leaves, long-stalked near the base and sheathed near the top of the stem. From late spring umbels of small white to cream flowers appear, followed in late summer or early autumn by pale, oblong fruits that are slightly curved and have five prominent ribs. The ripe fruits are popularly but incorrectly known as seeds.

GROWING TIPS Caraway tolerates most conditions but prefers moist soil and some sun. Sow the seed in summer or when it is ripe. Caraway is a decorative plant that grows vigorously and is self-seeding.

Cardamom

Elettaria cardamomum

Zingiberaceae

Lesser cardamom

Cardamom, an aromatic spice once considered an aphrodisiac, has been used since the fifth century BC. In India it is an essential ingredient of curries and pilaus, while in Saudi Arabia, cardamom is a traditional flavouring for coffee. Cardamom sweetens the breath, stimulates the appetite, and relieves flatulence.

HABITAT Native to East India and Sri Lanka. Found on hillsides in wet, mountain forests. Cultivated commercially in India and Guatemala.

DESCRIPTION Perennial bush to 2.4m(8ft) with smooth, green cane-like stems and large, dark green, leaf blades that are sheathed at the base. The flowering stems spread horizontally along the ground from the base of the stem and bear yellowish flowers with a purple lip. They are succeeded by oval pale green or brown fruits with dark brown aromatic seeds.

Cascara Sagrada

Rhamnus purshiana

Rhamnaceae

Buckthorn, sacred bark

Native Americans used the bark of this tree as a laxative and it soon became available as a propperietary remedy for chronic constipation. Extract of cascara sagrada is still used in laxatives but herbalists prefer the dried bark, which tones the intestinal muscles.

HABITAT Native North American tree occasionally found wild in mountains areas of the Pacific north-western states.

DESCRIPTION Deciduous tree to 8m(25ft) with chestnut coloured bark that may be covered with a grey-white lichen. The leaves are dark green, oval, and clustered at the ends of the branchlets. In spring, small greenish flowers grow in umbels, followed by pea-sized berries ripening from scarlet to black.

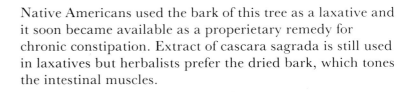

Catnip

Nepeta cataria

Labiatae

Catmint

Cats adore the strong aroma of this mint-like herb, hence the plant's common name. When bruised or cut, the scent of catmint has an aphrodisiac effect on cats who proceed to rub, twist, and roll themselves in the plant, eventually flattening it to the ground. Catmint-stuffed toy mice from pet stores hold a similar fascination for cats. According to an eighteenth-century British horticulturalist, cats will not destroy catmint that has been grown from seed – 'if you sow it, the cats won't know it'. Even so, catmint raised from seed is only protected so long as it remains completely intact. The scent has no such aphrodisiacal effect on humans.

Catmint leaves were once brewed as a tea, while the leaves were used in the Middle Ages to season meat and the young shoots added to salads. The tea is a traditional home remedy for stomach upsets, especially in children. Herbalists particularly recommend it for children's colic and diarrhoea. Catmint also promotes perspiration and a hot infusion is good for feverish colds and flu. Where there is insomnia due to restlessness, tension or anxiety, catmint's mild sedative action helps to induce sleep. Catmint leaves were once smoked to relieve bronchitis and the plant acquired a dubious reputation as a narcotic, probably due to a confusion with marijuana.

HABITAT Native to Europe and temperate Asia. Introduced in North America and other temperate zones. Widespread in central and southern parts of the UK. Grows on waste ground, field edges, railway banks, roadsides and in hedgerows. Prefers chalky or gravelly soil.

DESCRIPTION Mint-like perennial with a strong, rather disagreeable smell on hairy, branched stems from 30–100cm(1–3ft). The silvery grey leaves are coarsely toothed, heart-shaped and downy on the underside. From late spring to late summer, dense whorls of white two-lipped flowers appear towards the top of the stems. The upper lip is spotted with dark crimson to violet, and the anthers are deep red to purple. Bees are attracted to the flowers.

GROWING TIPS Sow seed in spring in a rich soil in a situation with some shade. Catmint can also be propagated by cuttings taken in summer. It is easy to grow and does not require as much watering as mint. Suitable for borders and rockeries as an ornamental, as well as the herb garden.

Cayenne

Capsicum frutescens

Solanaceae

Tabasco pepper, African pepper

Cayenne pepper took its name from Cayenne in French Guiana where supplies originated. The botanical name, *Capsicum*, also used to describe sweet bell peppers, is said to be derived from a Greek word meaning 'to bite' – a clear reference to its fierce taste. It is closely related to the other species of pepper, especially the sweet red and chilli pepper, *Capsicum annuum*, with which it may be confused. Bought cayenne may, in fact, contain ground sweet peppers or ground chilli peppers but is less fiery than some varieties of chilli. A traditional spice and condiment, cayenne is widely used in Creole, Cajun, Mexican and East Asian cuisines. In European and North American cookery the flavour of cayenne blends well with egg and cheese dishes, savoury sauces, and shellfish such as oysters. Cayenne is also the principle ingredient of hot tabasco sauce, hence its name Tabasco pepper. Small quantities of cayenne act as an appetite stimulant.

Cayenne is the species of capsicum that is used medicinally for its stimulant and antiseptic actions, as well as its digestive properties. Considered one of the best local and circulatory stimulants, cayenne may be used externally for poor circulation, unbroken chilblains, and pains associated with arthritis or lumbago. Internally, cayenne stimulates the heart, regulating the blood flow and strengthening the arteries and capillaries. At the onset of a cold, cayenne promotes perspiration and can increase the body's resistance to infection.

CAUTION Large doses of cayenne can severely irritate the gastro-intestinal system, and may also damage the liver and kidneys. Excessive or prolonged local application can cause blistering of the skin and dermatitis.

HABITAT Found wild in some tropical countries, notably South America (Brazil) and southern India. Supplies are said to have come originally from French Guiana. Now cultivated in South America, Africa, Asia and other tropical and subtropical countries. May be grown successfully in warmer, temperate climates.

DESCRIPTION Shrubby perennial plant from 30–90cm(1–3ft) with a woody trunk when mature, and angular, purple-tinged branches. The veined, stalked leaves take various forms but are usually elliptical and taper to a point. From early spring to early autumn, drooping white or yellowish flowers hang in twos or threes from long stalks. They are followed by small, brilliant oblong pods that ripen to red or orange. These 'peppers' have an aromatic smell and contain many flat seeds.

Celandine, Lesser

Ranunculus ficaria

Ranunculaceae

Pilewort

According to the doctrine of Signatures, the many swollen tubers of celandine root resembled piles. On account of its success in treating this ailment, the plant became known as pilewort, and even today herbalists recommend a celandine ointment or a poultice for external application to haemorrhoids.

HABITAT Native to Europe, western Asia, and North Africa. Widespread in moist meadows, ditches and hedgerows.

DESCRIPTION Familiar buttercup-like perennial with smooth, dark green, very glossy leaves that are sheathed at the base and heart-shaped. From early spring, solitary, star-like, bright-yellow flowers are borne on long stalks. The flowers have between eight and ten petals, whereas the buttercup has only five. The flowers close before rain or in dull weather and become bleached with age.

Celery, Wild

Apium graveolens

Umbelliferae

Smallage

Wild celery has a pungent smell and a bitter taste. It was popular with the Romans and widely used in medieval cooking. Celery seed was first used medicinally to ease rheumatic pains, gout and arthritis.

HABITAT Native to southern Europe. Found wild throughut Europe, Africa, North and South America, along tidal rivers and marshy ground near the sea.

DESCRIPTION Strong-smelling bienial with a bulbous fleshy root and coarse, ridged and branched stems from 30–60cm(1–2ft). The yellow-green to dark green leaves are opposite, dentate and very similar to those of garden celery. Throughout the summer sparse umbels of greenish-white flowers appear, followed by small, oval fruit (seeds).

Centaury

Centaurium erythraea/Erythraea centaurium

Gentianaceae

Common centaury, European centaury

Centaury is named after the famous centaur of Greek myth, Chiron. Half-human and half-horse, Chiron was a wise healer who is said to have discovered the medicinal use of plants. *Erythrae* is from a Greek word meaning red and refers to the colour of the flowers. According to the early Celts, centaury brought luck, while Saxon herbalists recommended it for snake bites. During the Middle Ages it was considered a magical herb that had the power to ward off evil spirits. Centaury blossoms are carved on the tomb of the famous English poet, Wordsworth. For him, the flowers, which open only in fine weather, resembled the rising sun.

Bitterwort was an old English name for centaury and its extreme bitterness led Culpeper to pronounce it 'very wholesome, but not very toothsome'. Like other members of the gentian family, to which it belongs, centaury contains several bitter compounds. These have a tonic effect on the digestive system via their beneficial action on the liver and gall bladder. Taken before meals centaury stimulates a flagging appetite; after meals it eases dyspepsia and heartburn. Indeed centaury's digestive properties have long been valued, especially in France and Italy. It is one of the bitter herbs used in vermouths, drunk as aperitifs to encourage the appetite or act on a sluggish liver. Centaury has also found its way from traditional herbalism to the more alternative system developed by Dr Edward Bach (1886–1936). Centaury, one of the 38 Bach Flower Remedies, is recommended for quiet people who are anxious to please and easily dominated by others.

HABITAT Central European native, widespread from western Europe to western Siberia. Introduced elsewhere. Found in dry, grassy places, roadsides and chalky slopes.

DESCRIPTION Annual with erect, square stem from 15–30cm(6–12in) that branches near the top. The leaves at the base of the stem form a rosette; the stem leaves are smaller, pale green, lance-shaped and arranged in pairs at intervals. From late summer to mid-autumn the stem is crowned with clusters of attractive rosy pink, star-like flowers with yellow stamens.

Chamomile, German

Matricaria chamomilla or *Matricaria recutita*

Compositae
Wild chamomile

German chamomile is said to have been introduced into that country from its native Spain. According to some authorities, German chamomile is not a true chamomile, botanically speaking. It is, however, this species of chamomile that is preferred by both medical herbalists and homeopaths. *Matricaria* is derived from either *mater*, the Latin word for mother, or *matrix*, meaning womb. Both derivations point to chamomile's traditional use for female complaints including menstrual cramps, sore nipples and thrush. Chamomile's medicinal properties reside in the blue volatile oil present in the flowers that are used to treat a wide range of ailments. A tea made from the flower heads is particularly good for such digestive problems as an upset stomach, heartburn and flatulence. Chamomile tea is also well known for its relaxing, sleep-inducing properties that help to alleviate insomnia, headaches and anxiety. It is a gentle remedy that can be used with confidence to calm restless children. Indeed, in homeopathy, chamomile is particularly valued for treating children's complaints including teething, earache, colic and headaches. An extraordinarily versatile herb, chamomile also has soothing antiseptic properties and may be applied externally to ulcers, burns and eczema.

As a cosmetic, chamomile's soothing action makes it particularly suitable for sensitive skins. Healing to the mucous membrane of the skin, chamomile is mild enough for those with ageing or dry and delicate skins, as well as those with sensitive skin prone to allergic reactions.

HABITAT Native to Europe and northern Asia. Introduced in North America. Widespread in meadows, along roadsides, and on waste ground. Prefers light but moist soil. Cultivated commercially in Central Europe, particularly Germany.

DESCRIPTION Sweet delicately scented annual of the daisy family with smooth, branching stems to 60cm(2ft). The bright green leaves are deeply incised into thread-like segments and have no stalks. Single daisy-like flowers appear on long stalks from early summer to mid-autumn. The blossoms may be distinguished from the garden chamomiles by their yellow centres, which are markedly conical and hollow.

GROWING TIPS Sow seed in late summer or early autumn in light but moist soil. Chamomile likes a sunny position.

Chamomile, Roman
Chamaemelum nobile

Compositae
Garden chamomile, Roman chamomile

Garden chamomile takes its botanical and common names from the Greek word for the plant, *chamaemelon*. This translates as 'apple on the ground' and describes the distinctive sweet, apple scent given off by all parts of the herb. In the Middle Ages, chamomile was strewn about the floor of the home to sweeten the air. It is traditionally planted along garden walls and lawns instead of grass: its sweet fragrance fills the air when trodden underfoot, and, like grass, the plant suffers no lasting damage.

Garden chamomile was known to the ancient Egyptians who considered it a cure-all and dedicated it to Ra, the sun god. Chamomile possesses similar properties to German chamomile and is popularly taken as a tea, made either from fresh or dried flowers. It is particularly good for indigestion and heartburn, and has a soothing and relaxing effect. Chamomile is widely available in tea bags and may be taken for tense, nervous headaches, or as a bedtime drink where there is sleeplessness. Chamomile was an ingredient of herbal beers and imparted its delicate flavour to the type of Spanish sherry known as *manzanilla*, or little apple.

Like German chamomile, garden chamomile has cosmetic uses. An infusion of the herb makes a gentle, non-chemical lightner for fair hair, and it is a popular ingredient of herbal shampoos. Added to the bath, dried chamomile flowers or essential oil of chamomile are particularly calming for those suffering from nervous tension. The flowers are often included in pot pourri.

HABITAT Native to southern Europe and widespread over Europe and southern England on rough, dry pastures with sandy soil. Introduced elsewhere. Grown commercially in Central Europe and cultivated horticulturally. A double variety may be produced from the single type.

DESCRIPTION Apple-scented, low-growing perennial to 30cm(12in) with trailing, branched and hairy stems. The leaves, like German chamomile, are deeply incised and finely feathery in appearance but greyer green and rather downy. The daisy-like flowers with yellow conical centres appear from mid-summer to mid-autumn on erect stalks. This variety has a much stronger fragrance than German chamomile.

Chervil

Anthriscus cerefolium

Umbelliferae

Garden chervil

Garden chervil is closely related to *Anthriscus sylvestris* or common cow parsley, sometimes known as wild chervil. Garden chervil is, however, found wild only as an escape from cultivation. It is a graceful, sweet-smelling herb with a subtle, sweetish flavour reminiscent of anise or liquorice. Introduced to Britain by the Romans, chervil is still widely used in European cuisines but is less popular in Britain and the USA. Chervil is particularly relished by the French who consider it an alternative to parsley for flavouring and garnishing. An ingredient of the classic *fines herbes* flavouring for omelettes, chervil is necessary for *béarnaise* sauce and is often added to vinaigrettes. Chervil is very versatile and its subtle flavour will complement many dishes. It must, however, be used fresh as its delicate flavour is lost on drying and with long cooking.

Chervil was once considered a cleansing spring herb that made a welcome change after a heavy winter diet with few, if any, fresh green vegetables. Chervil stimulates the appetite and aids digestion while its mild diuretic qualities help to cleanse the system. The fresh juice was taken as a blood purifier in spring and for gout and gall-bladder problems. Warm poultices of chervil were formerly applied to bruises and painful joints. Today, chervil is rarely used medicinally.

HABITAT Native to the Middle East, south-east Europe, and Asia. Naturalized in North America and cultivated in temperate and warm climates, especially France. Prefers light, well-drained soils.

DESCRIPTION Aromatic annual to 45cm(18in) with slightly hairy, finely grooved, branching stems. The delicate leaves, similar to those of cow parsley, are pale green, deeply divided, and fern-like. Lacy white flowers appear in flat umbels from late spring to mid-summer.

GROWING TIPS Sow seed in late summer in light, well-drained soil. The plant needs warmth and shelter in the winter and some shade and moisture in summer. It grows well in window boxes, but without too much direct sunlight. Cut back regularly to stop chervil running to seed.

Chickweed

Stellaria media

Caryophyllaceae
Starweed

As the name suggests, chickweed was traditionally fed to poultry, and wild birds feed on its green tops and fresh seed. Fresh chickweed is a traditional home remedy for healing cuts, sores and inflammations, and a chickweed poultice is said to draw out infection from boils and abcesses.

HABITAT Native to Europe but widely distributed all over the world. Naturalized in North America and Australia. A common weed on cultivated land and wasteland.

DESCRIPTION Ubiquitous annual with branched, straggling stems from 10–40cm(4–16in) that trail along the ground. The leaves are oval with long stalks and succulent, like the stems. From early spring to late autumn numerous small, white five-petalled flowers appear that resemble stars.

Chicory

Cichorium intybus

Compositae
Wild succory

The ancient Egyptians and Arabs ate blanched chicory leaves, and the roasted ground root has been used to flavour coffee since the early nineteenth century. Queen Elizabeth I took chicory soup for its health-giving properties, and today herbalists value chicory for its tonic effect on the liver.

HABITAT Native to Europe and naturalized in North America. Common on roadsides, waste ground and field edges on light, sandy soil.

DESCRIPTION Perennial to 1.2m(4ft) on a large tap root. The bristly stem bears stiff, green, twig-like branches that are almost leafless towards the top. The jagged lower leaves are rough with hairs underneath. Large, sky-blue, dandelion-shaped flowers blossom from late summer to mid-autumn, closing up towards noon.

Chives

Allium schoenoprasum

Liliaceae
Cives

It is said that chives have a particularly long culinary history that dates back to ancient China in 3000 BC. The only member of the onion family to be gathered from the wild, chives were not cultivated until the Middle Ages but have enjoyed widespread popularity ever since. Named the 'Infant Onion' because of the smallness of the bulb, the flavour of chives is much milder than that of the onion and may even be tolerated by those who either dislike onions or find them difficult to digest. In the kitchen, chives are ideal for flavouring soft cheeses, new and baked potatoes, omelettes and salads. An ingredient of tartare sauce, chives can be added to many soups, sauces and salad dressings. For grilled fish and meat, herb butters that include chives are particularly good. The small bulbs can also be pickled.

HABITAT Native to temperate and northern Europe. Introduced and naturalized in North America. Occasionally found wild in rocky, limestone soils but also grows on stream banks and damp grassland. Cultivated widely both commercially and horticulturally throughout northern Europe and North America.

DESCRIPTION Hardy perennial and smallest member of the onion family, growing to a height of 25–30cm(10–12in). The hollow, grass-like, tubular leaves grow in clumps from small flattish bulbs. In summer the flowering stem produces a spherical head of numerous pale mauve flowers. These conceal seed vessels containing small black seeds.

GROWING TIPS Chives are easily grown either in the garden or in pots indoors. They will tolerate most ordinary garden soils but prefer a medium loam and a semi-shaded position. Sow seed in spring or propagate by dividing clumps in spring or autumn. Snip off the flowering stems to encourage leaf growth. Chives lose their flavour on drying but can be kept for two or three weeks in a plastic bag or box in the fridge. The leaves can also be quick frozen. Chives make a pretty ornamental edging plant for the herb garden.

Cinnamon

Cinnamomum zeylanicum

Lauraceae

Ceylon cinnamon

Cinnamon originally came to Europe from Sri Lanka via the eastern spice routes. The Portuguese considered the spice valuable enough to warrant an occupation of Sri Lanka in the mid-sixteenth century. They were succeeded by the Dutch who began large-scale cinnamon cultivation on the island in 1770. Cinnamon itself consists of the inner bark of cinnamon tree branches, which curls up to form thin rolls or quills when dried in the sun. It has long been used to flavour biscuits, puddings and cakes in European cuisines, and is an important ingredient of the spicy mulled wines drunk in winter. In Arabian dishes, however, cinnamon adds flavour to savoury meat dishes, and is commonly found in Indian curries and pilaus. Good-quality cinnamon sticks retain their flavour better than the ground spice, and are particularly good stirred into fresh coffee. Cinnamon tastes similar to cassia (*Cinnamonum cassia*), a close relative, but its more delicate flavour is considered superior.

Although cinnamon is used mainly for culinary purposes, its warming action makes it a valuable home remedy for colds and chills. Like many other kitchen spices, cinnamon is helpful for indigestion and diarrhoea. It will also stop vomiting and relieve feelings of nausea. The volatile oil obtained from cinnamon bark has antibacterial properties that help to prevent food poisoning, especially in hot, humid countries where food, especially meat, is liable to go off. In such cuisines, cinnamon is used both as a flavouring and a preservative to discourage bacterial infection. Centuries ago, the ancient Egyptians included cinnamon in their embalming mixtures for its preservative action.

HABITAT Native of Sri Lanka, and also found wild in tropical forests in South India and Malaysia. Cultivated commercially in Sri Lanka, India, the West Indies, Brazil and other tropical climates. Prefers sandy soils and a sheltered position.

DESCRIPTION Evergreen tree from 6–10m(18–30ft) that belongs to the laurel family. The bark is thick, pale and somewhat cork-like on the outside, and the branches are strong and speckled with orange. The leathery ovate leaves are opposite with shiny green uppers on maturing, and paler undersides. They have a rather spicy smell. In summer small yellowish-white flowers hang in clusters from long stalks. These are followed by oval blue berries with white spots.

Cinquefoil

Potentilla reptans/canadensis

Rosaceae

Five-finger grass, five-leaf grass

Cinquefoil was a popular ingredient of love potions during the Middle Ages. Witches also used the plant in spells, possibly because frogs are said to like sitting upon the leaves. One appalling magical ointment is said to have been prepared by mixing cinquefoil juice, lovage and aconite with 'the fat of children dug up from their graves and added to fine wheat flour' (quoted by Mrs Grieve in *A Modern Herbal*, 1931).

    Cinquefoil was used medicinally as early as the first century AD, when it was employed in the treatment of malaria. Culpeper prescribed the fresh herb for fevers and to cool the blood. The herb also has a diuretic action and the root was once employed to stop internal bleeding and for diarrhoea. Today, some herbalists still recommend a mouthwash of the dried North American plant for ulcers.

DESCRIPTION Creeping perennial on branched rootstock with thread-like stems to 1m(3ft). The leaves are divided into five, sparsely hairy leaflets with serrated edges and prominent veins on the undersides. Yellow flowers, like those of the silverweed, bloom from early summer.

HABITAT European (*reptans*) and North American (*canadensis*) native. Common in hedgerows and grassy places.

Cleavers

Galium aparine

Rubiaceae

Goosegrass, grip grass, sticky Willie

Most of cleavers' common names reflect its tendency to stick to anything that passes. Geese are said to be partial to the stems, hence the name goosegrass. Cleavers has been widely used in herbal medicine for centuries, on account of the tonic, blood-purifying, and diuretic properties of the fresh plant. In spring, after a starchy winter diet, the fresh green tops were made into a cleansing drink. An infusion of cleavers is a traditional remedy for skin eruptions, while its diuretic properties are helpful for urinary problems. Modern herbalists value cleavers' tonic effect on the lymphatic system. This encourages the elimination of toxins and explains the cleansing reputation of the herb.

    Cleavers seed was once dried and roasted for use as a coffee substitute. According to Linnaeus, Swedish farmers

made the stems into a crude sieve for straining milk. Cosmetically, a cleavers rinse may help to clear up dandruff.

HABITAT European native and naturalized in North America. A common weed of hedgerows, roadsides and the edges of fields and gardens.

DESCRIPTION Annual with trailing, straggling stems to 120cm(4ft) and narrow, lance-shaped leaves in whorls of six. Both stem and leaves are covered with rough, hooked bristles. Star-shaped, greenish-white flowers appear in summer followed by small, round seed balls covered, like the stems, with the hooked bristles.

Cloves

Eugenia aromatica or *Szygium aromaticum*

Myrtaceae
Clove tree

Cloves are the dried, unopened flower buds from the tropical clove tree. They were known to the ancient Chinese and were being transported along the old spice routes into Rome by the fourth century. Clove trees originated in a small group of islands known as the Moluccas and open hostilities erupted among European countries, notably Holland, France, and Portugal, over who should control this lucrative trade from these islands. The French introduced clove trees to Mauritius, and at the beginning of the nineteenth century cultivation started in Zanzibar.

The pungent flavour of cloves is due to an essential oil that has powerful antiseptic properties. It is recorded that during the time of the ancient Han dynasty in China, it was customary to chew a clove when addressing a royal personage. Cloves do in fact sweeten the breath and are frequently added to toothpastes and powders for their antiseptic action. Clove oil is also mildly anaesthetic and is invaluable for toothache. Like the other common kitchen spices, cloves aid the digestion of food and prevent flatulence; they also help to relieve nausea and vomiting. Cloves' strong antiseptic action is particularly useful for preserving foods in countries where the climate is hot and humid. Commonly used in pickles, curries, and with such meats as ham and beef, cloves serve a double purpose: they help to prevent food spoiling as well as adding aroma and flavour. Cloves are traditionally added to apple pies and mulled wines. In the home, clove-studded oranges, called pomanders, fulfill the dual function of sweetening stale air and repelling moths.

HABITAT Native to the islands of South-east Asia, notably the Moluccas. Introduced to the West Indies and the tropical East African islands, Zanzibar and Madagascar. Cultivated in wet tropical countries on sea coasts.

DESCRIPTION Very aromatic evergreen tree to 10m(30ft) that is a neat pyramid shape. The trunk and branches are covered with smooth, greyish bark and the oblong leaves are shiny, bright green and taper to a point. The leaves grow in pairs and are fragrant when bruised. Long, green flower-buds grow in clusters at the ends of the branches, turning into fresh-smelling, pale pink, peach- or crimson-tinted blossoms.

Coltsfoot

Tussilago farfara

Compositae

Son-before-father, coughwort, horse's hoof

Coltsfoot and horse's hoof refer to the hoof-like shape of the leaves, while son-before-father nicely describes the plant's habit of flowering before the leaves appear. Indeed, some early botanists thought that coltsfoot had no leaves at all. The botanical name *Tussilago* is a Latin word meaning 'cough relieving', and from it we get the medical term tussis, meaning cough. Coltsfoot's particular combination of expectorant properties with a soothing, healing action has assured its position as an important remedy for coughs. In former times, the most popular method to relieve coughing was to smoke dried coltsfoot leaves as a tobacco, and today coltsfoot may still be included in herbal smoking mixtures. In the home, coltsfoot tea and coltsfoot syrup were standard remedies for coughs, bronchitis and asthma. Coltsfoot was also made into a medicinal candy, known as coltsfoot rock, possibly to make it more palatable to children. In Paris, coltsfoot was such a highly esteemed remedy that a flower was customarily painted over pharmacy doors. Some modern herbalists recommend an infusion of coltsfoot for all respiratory ailments, while others, influenced by toxicity tests on the flowers, consider it an unsafe remedy. Coltsfoot leaves have been discovered to contain useful quantities of zinc. This mineral has anti-inflammatory properties and explains why the fresh leaves were once applied externally to boils and abcesses.

CAUTION In view of the controversy surrounding this herb, it should be used use only as directed by a qualified practitioner.

HABITAT Native to Europe, northern and western Asia, and North Africa. Introduced and naturalized in North America, from Nova Scotia southwards to West Virginia. Grows abundantly on waste ground, railway embankments, and on hard, bare, shingly ground.

DESCRIPTION Perennial to 25cm(9in) on spreading, white root with creeping horizontal stems. The jagged, dandelion-like leaves on long stalks are covered with white, felted hairs when young. From early spring and before the leaves appear, single daisy-type yellow flowers appear at the ends of scaly, purplish stems. These are followed by seeds covered with tufts of silky, white hairs.

Comfrey

Symphytum officinale

Boraginaceae

Knitbone, bruisewort

Both the botanical and common names of comfrey testify to its healing properties. *Symphytum* is derived from a Greek word meaning to join or unite, and in the Middle Ages comfrey was widely employed to mend or knit together broken bones. Comfrey was commonly grown in cottage gardens, and poultices of the fresh leaves are a traditional home remedy of long standing for sprains, bruises, and cuts. Comfrey not only promotes the healing of tissue and bone, but at the same time reduces swelling, effectively speeding up the healing process. The celebrated herbalists Gerard and Culpeper prescribed comfrey for internal as well as external use. Gerard recommended a comfrey-root syrup for ulcers of the lungs, while Culpeper considered it 'very effectual in inward hurts' and attributed its wound-healing and bone-knitting qualities to the influence of Saturn, planetary ruler of the skin and the skeleton. Comfrey's remarkable healing powers have been attributed to its high content of allantoin, a substance that promotes the growth of tissue, bone and cartilage, both internally and externally. Comfrey root and leaves are also particularly rich in mucilage, a gelatinous substance that binds and holds fractures and broken bones, as well as soothing inflamed and painful tissues. Homeopaths, too, acknowledge comfrey's impressive healing attributes, and prescribe it for fractures, broken bones, and joint troubles.

CAUTION Recent American research has fuelled a continuing debate over the safety of taking comfrey internally over a long period.

HABITAT Native to Europe and temperate regions of Asia. Introduced and naturalized in the USA. Found in the rich, wet soils along stream and river banks, in ditches and in damp meadowland.

DESCRIPTION Perennial to 1m(3ft) on thick, dark brown rootstock. The stout, hollow stem and the leaves are rough with hairs like borage. The ovate lower leaves are very large, the upper leaves are smaller, narrower and taper to a point. From early summer to early autumn, clusters of drooping flowers grow down one side of short, curved stalks. The flowers are bell-shaped and range in colour from creamy yellow to mauve or pale pink.

GROWING TIPS Comfrey is hardy enough to survive most conditions but for best results, sow the seed in spring to summer in a rich, moist soil in a sunny position. Cut back the leaves two or three times a year and use for compost.

Coriander

Coriandrum sativum

Umbelliferae

Chinese parsley

Coriander has been used both as a flavouring and a medicine for over 3000 years. Its use is recorded in several ancient texts including the Egyptian Ebers Papyrus and the Book of Exodus. The word coriander is derived from the Greek *koris*, meaning bug, since the plant was supposed to possess an insect-like smell reminiscent of bed bugs. Coriander has always been a favourite culinary herb in the East and was introduced to Europe by the Romans. The green, parsley-like leaves have a fragrant, strongly aromatic taste that lends a characteristic flavour to curries and chutneys. They are extensively used in Chinese and south-east Asian cookery, hence the common name Chinese parsley. Coriander was popular in English cuisine up to Elizabethan times, and is now enjoying a revival, especially as a flavouring for soups and salads. The dried, ripe seeds have a sweeter, spicier taste than the fresh leaf and are a feature of Indian, North African and Indonesian cuisines. In parts of Europe, coriander seed flavours bread, cakes and liqueurs. It is also a traditional pickling spice.

Coriander seed aids the digestion of food, easing colic and flatulence. Coriander-seed water was once a popular gripe water for children.

HABITAT Native to the Mediterranean region and the Middle East. Widespread in many temperate zones in dry soils. Occasionally found wild in Britain. Cultivated commercially in India, parts of South America, Morocco and in South Carolina in the USA.

DESCRIPTION Hardy annual to 60cm(2ft). The slender, branched stem bears flat, parsley-like lower leaves and feathery, thread-like upper leaves. The leaves are aromatic when crushed. Small, flat umbels of pretty white to pale mauve flowers bloom from mid-summer to mid-autumn followed by round, green berries (known as seeds) that drop as soon as they ripen.

GROWING TIPS Sow the seed in late spring or autumn in shallow rows. Germination may be slow. Coriander needs a dry, light soil and a sunny, sheltered position.

Costmary

Chrysanthemum balsamita

Compositae

Alecost, bible-leaf

Perfumed toilet water was once made from costmary leaves and they added a spicy flavour to ale. Costmary was known as bible-leaf because the early American settlers used the long leaves as bookmarks, reviving themselves with the pleasant scent or nibbling a leaf during lengthy sermons.

HABITAT Native to southern Europe and western Asia. Naturalized and cultivated in North America and Europe.

DESCRIPTION Perennial to 1m(3ft) with wide, grey-green, ovate, sweet-smelling leaves that have serrated edges. The yellow, button-like flowers resemble those of tansy and appear in loose clusters from late summer to early autumn.

Couch Grass

Agropyron repens

Graminaeae

Twitch grass, dog's grass

This common weed is a soothing urinary antiseptic, used to treat cystitis and prostate trouble. Ailing dogs are said to eat the grass to make themselves sick.

HABITAT Widespread European native. Naturalized in North America, especially the eastern states. A troublesome weed and common on arable land, waste ground and sandy places.

DESCRIPTION Perennial grass with a creeping underground rootstock that extends to 120cm(4ft). The smooth, hollow stems have greenish-grey flat leaves that have roughish upper surfaces. Dense two-rowed spikes of small purple flowers bloom from mid-summer to early autumn.

Cowslip

Primula veris

Primulaceae

Key flower, herb Peter

Cowslip is thought to be a corruption of cowlsop, a reference to the dry meadows grazed by cattle that are the plant's favoured habitat. Key flower and herb Peter, the cowslip's common names, refer to the resemblance of the flowers to bunches of keys, and the legendary origin of the plant: it sprang up where St Peter dropped the keys to heaven. Cowslip flowers make an excellent wine with calming properties, and cowslip tea is a soothing, traditional remedy for restlessness, nervous headaches and insomnia. Cowslip root is expectorant and was once used to treat bronchitis.

HABITAT Native to northern and central Europe. Once common on porous chalky soils in grassy meadows and pasture land. Now becoming scarce due to over picking and pesticides.

DESCRIPTION Perennial to 30cm(12in) resembling the primrose but with shorter, more rounded leaves covered in fine hairs. The leaves form a rosette that lies almost flat on the ground. Rising from the centre, the long, slender stem is topped with clusters of pretty, nodding, pale yellow flowers usually spotted with orange.

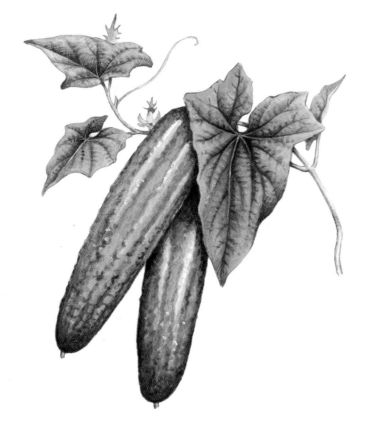

Cucumber

Cucumis sativus

Cucurbitaceae

The cucumber has been in cultivation for around 3000 years. The seeds may expel tapeworms but the fruit is principally employed in skin preparations for its cooling and softening effect. Fresh cucumber slices refresh sore, tired eyes.

HABITAT Native to the East Indies. Widely cultivated.

DESCRIPTION Familiar trailing annual with climbing tendrils. The leaves are heart-shaped and the flowers yellow and bell-shaped. The ridged green fruit is well known.

Dandelion

Taraxacum officinale

Compositae

Piss-a-bed

The dandelion acquired its name from a fancied resemblance between its jagged leaves and a lion's teeth – in French, *dents de lion*. The botanical name *Taraxacum*, from the Greek *taraxos* and *achos* meaning, respectively, disorder and remedy, points to the medicinal value of the herb. In the sixteenth century, dandelion became known as *herba urinaria* because of the strong diuretic action of the leaves, a property still clearly reflected in its country name, piss-a-bed (in French, *pissenlit*). Unlike diuretic drugs, dandelion, a good natural source of potassium, does not deplete the body's potassium supplies. The dandelion has sustained its strong medicinal reputation since its introduction by eleventh-century Arabian physicians: modern herbalists still recommend dandelion for water retention and liver ailments. Dandelion also has a reputation as a blood-cleanser and is considered helpful for skin diseases and rheumatism.

Young dandelion leaves are traditionally eaten in salads for their chicory-like taste. The flowers have been made into a potent wine, and the root, leaves and flowers brewed into a variety of tonic beers, such as dandelion and burdock. Dandelion roots may also be eaten boiled or fried, but they are more usually roasted to produce an excellent coffee substitute that is naturally caffeine-free. The wide range of dandelion coffee available at health food stores is testimony to the dandelion's continuing popularity.

HABITAT Native to Europe and Asia. Introduced in many countries including North America and Australia. Common on soils rich in nitrogen in any situation.

DESCRIPTION Common perennial on thick taproot to 30cm(12in). A basal rosette of hairless, dark green leaves with large, jagged teeth rises straight from the root. From the centre grows a purplish, hollow flower stalk containing a milky juice. The familiar yellow flowers bloom from late spring to mid-summer followed by the seed head or 'clock' – a round ball of wispy, plumed seeds that can travel up to six miles in the wind.

Dill

Anethum graveolens

Umbelliferae
Dill weed

Dill's use is recorded in the Bible and it was well known to the ancient Greeks and Romans. Introduced into Europe during the Middle Ages, dill became popular in Scandinavian countries and its name, according to some authorities, is derived from an old Norse word *dilla* meaning 'to lull'. Dill seeds contain a volatile oil that calms and settles the stomach, easing flatulence and colic. Dill water was once very popular for treating griping and colic in babies and small children, and the herb is also reputed to promote the flow of milk in nursing mothers. Dill seeds, once popularly known as 'Meeting House' seeds, were chewed during long church services to allay hunger pains and calm rumbling stomachs.

Dill is an important culinary herb. The fresh green leaves have a sharp, slightly sweetish tang that is unfortunately lost on drying. They are traditionally served with fish, particularly poached salmon, and with potato salads. In Scandinavian and Polish cuisines, dill is used like parsley for flavouring sour cream, sauces, vegetables and as a garnish. The seeds are as popular as the leaf, although they have a very different taste that is rather like caraway. Dill seeds, or sometimes the whole plant with its ripe seeds, are a classic ingredient of pickled gherkins and cucumbers.

HABITAT Native to the Mediterranean and southern Russia. Found wild in the Mediterranean in cultivated fields. Naturalized in North America. Widely cultivated and popular in herb gardens.

DESCRIPTION Aromatic annual to 1m(3ft), resembling fennel in appearance but smaller. The stems are smooth and shiny and the leaves pale green and very feathery. In mid- to late summer flat umbels of small yellow flowers appear; the petals are turned inwards. They are followed by large quantities of oval, flat fruits, popularly called seeds.

GROWING TIPS Dill is a hardy plant, germinating quickly from seed sown in spring. Thin out the young plants and water frequently in dry weather. Dill prefers a sunny spot that is sheltered from the wind, and will often seed itself.

Dog's Mercury

Mercurialis perennis

Euphorbiaceae

In old herbals dog's mercury is credited with remarkable healing powers, allegedly revealed by the Roman god Mercury. It is a poisonous plant with an acrid juice that once served as an antiseptic and a wart remover. Today, dog's mercury is little used.

HABITAT European native common in woods and shady ground. Grows wild in the eastern USA.

DESCRIPTION Fetid-smelling perennial with a round, grooved stem. The roughish, dark green leaves are opposite and ovate with serrated edges. Small greenish flowers grow from the leaf axils, just before the leaves have fully opend, from early to late spring.

Dog Rose

Rosa canina

Rosaceae

Briar rose

According to folklore, wild white roses were once so common in England that the country became known as Albion, from *alba*, the Latin for white. The plant's common and botanical names allude to a medieval belief that the plant cured rabid dog bites. Today, it is valued for its hips, rich in vitamin C. These were collected from the wild during World War II when citrus fruit was scarce, and are popularly drunk as a tea.

HABITAT Native to Europe, North Africa and western Asia. Naturalized in North America. Common in hedgerows, thickets, and scrubland.

DESCRIPTION Climbing rose with very prickly stems that grows to 3m(10ft). The bright green leaves are oval, finely serrated and taper to a point. The delicate, sweet-scented flowers appear from mid- to late summer and vary in colour from white to palest pink. They are quickly followed by deep red, fleshy hips.

Dyer's Greenweed

Genista tinctoria

Leguminosae

Dyer's broom

The flowering tops of dyer's greenweed yield a yellow dye that was widely used to colour wool, linen and leather. The fresh plant has diuretic properties and was used medicinally to treat gout and rheumatism, while the seeds were mixed into a plaster to set broken limbs.

HABITAT Native to the Mediterranean and western Asia. Naturalized in North America. Grows wild in heathland and rough pasture land.

DESCRIPTION Perennial broom-like shrub to 60cm(2ft) with erect, stiff branches bearing simple, alternate, spear-shaped leaves. From mid-summer to early autumn, bright yellow, pea-like flowers grow in thick spikes at the ends of the shoots, followed by smooth seed pods that ripen to brown.

Echinacea

Echinacea angustifolia

Compositae

Purple coneflower, Kansas snakeroot

Early American settlers learned from native plains Indians of echinacea's reputation for healing wounds and snake bites. The root has long been regarded as an excellent blood cleanser for clearing up septic sores, boils and abcesses. Modern research has corroborated the root's anti-bacterial effect and herbalists believe that echinacea strengthens the immune system.

HABITAT Native to the North American prairies as far north as southern Canada.

DESCRIPTION Perennial on thick, bristly stem to 45cm(18in) with ovate leaves that tape to a sharp point at both ends. From early summer to early autumn, faintly aromatic, solitary flowers appear on stout stalks. The purple centres are distinctly conical in shape and surrounded by dullish purple ray florets.

Elder

Sambucus nigra

Caprifoliaceae

Pipe tree, bour tree

Elder is derived from an Anglo-Saxon word for fire, and it is said that the young branches were hollowed out to make a primitive form of bellows. They also served as whistles and children's blowpipes, hence the common names pipe tree and bour (bore) tree. The elder has long been associated with sorrow and grief: Judas was said to have hanged himself from an elder, and Christ's cross was reputedly fashioned from its wood. In Scandinavian fairy tales, the elder was a magical tree and the dwelling place of the Elder-tree mother whose permission must be sought before any part of the tree could be cut down for wood. In Britain, elders were often planted near cottages so that the owners, having first annointed their eyes with elder juice, could see if any witches were approaching. Elder branches were also buried alongside the dead to protect their souls from the devil.

Known as the 'medicine chest of country people', virtually every part of the elder had its use. The fine-grained wood furnished combs and musical instruments, while a syrup made from the berries was an excellent cordial for colds. The flowers promote sweating and are a traditional home remedy for colds and the early stages of influenza. 'Composition essence', a herbal cold cure, is based on elderflower and peppermint. In the kitchen, elder flowers make an excellent sparkling wine, gooseberry and elderflower preserve, and sweet elder-flower fritters. Elderflower water is a skin tonic of long standing, while, more recently, the flowers have found their way into cosmetic eye gels for disguising eye wrinkles. An infusion of bruised elder leaves dabbed on the skin will help to deter flying insects.

HABITAT Native to Europe, western Asia and North Africa. Introduced and naturalized in North America. Common in hedgerows, copses, the edges of woods and near dwellings. Prefers moist soils.

DESCRIPTION Familiar, fast-growing shrub or small tree to 7m(24ft) with a cork-like bark. The dark green leaves are grouped in fives with finely serrated edges and taper to a point. In summer, tiny sweet-smelling, creamy-white flowers grow in flat-topped umbels, followed by drooping bunches of small, juicy, purple-black berries.

Elecampane

Inula helenium

Compositae

Scabwort

Elecampane was familiar to the ancient Celts and Anglo-Saxons as well as the Greeks and Romans. According to some authorities, the specific botanical name *helenium* refers to Helen of Troy. It is Helen's plant, springing from her tears when she was abducted by Paris. Culpeper set elecampane under the dominion of the planet Mercury, associated with the voice and lungs through its rulership of the sign Gemini. He prescribed it for 'coughs, shortness of breath and wheezing in the lungs'. More recent analysis of the active principle in elecampane root, inulin, has found it to be a powerful expectorant for expelling fluid from the lungs, and so the plant has maintained its age-old reputation as one of the most effective herbal remedies for respiratory disorders, especially bronchitis. Elecampane's common name, scabwort, bears testimony to inulin's antibacterial properties: it was formerly used to treat scab, a disease afflicting sheep.

In Elizabethan England, elecampane roots were sugared and eaten as a sweetmeat, while in Switzerland, the root extract was used as a flavouring for the liqueur Absinthe. Elecampane root also has aromatic, tonic properties that are helpful for indigestion. According to a seventeenth-century recipe, elecampane root steeped in white port, sugar and currants, was particularly good for colic.

HABITAT Native to Central and southern Europe. Naturalized in North America, from Nova Scotia to North Carolina. Widespread on damp soils in shady hedgerows, along roadsides, and on waste ground. Prefers shady situations.

DESCRIPTION Tall, striking plant with stout, hairy stems to 1.5m(5ft) growing from a thick, brown, aromatic taproot. The large leaves, up to 30cm(12in) in length, are hairy above, downy beneath and pointed. The lower leaves have long stalks, the upper are stalkless. From early to late summer bright yellow, ragged, sunflower-like blossoms enclosed by downy bracts appear on long stalks.

GROWING TIPS Propagate from root cuttings taken in autumn. Cover and store in the warmth until spring, then plant out in a moist but well-drained loamy soil. Elecampane prefers a shady position.

Eucalyptus
Eucalyptus globulus

Myrtaceae
Tasmanian blue gum

Eucalyptus comes from a Greek word meaning covering or lid, because the flower buds are enclosed in a kind of membrane. *Globulus* or little globe, the name given to the species by a French botanist, refers to the cup-shaped fruits that were said to resemble a button once fashionable in France. Eucalyptus stores large amounts of water in its roots and was planted in swampy 'fever districts' to dry up the marshes and prevent outbreaks of malaria. Native Australian aborigines discovered the medicinal properties of eucalyptus oil, and this strongly antiseptic substance found its way into Europe in the mid-nineteenth century. Both orthodox and herbal medicine continue to acknowledge blue gum's antibacterial and astringent qualities and the oil is commonly found in proprietary throat lozenges, cold remedies and toothpastes. Inhalations of the oil are particularly beneficial for colds and catarrh. For its germicidal properties, eucalyptus oil was once widely used by vets to kill fleas and lice.

The blue gum has become the dominant broad-leafed tree in Australia and is an excellent source of timber. In parts of South America and Africa, eucalyptus plantations have been established for soil drainage and to prevent erosion. Planting eucalyptus trees for paper pulp has, however, provoked severe criticism from environmentalists since, in some parts of the world, virgin forest has been cut down to make way for this fast-growing, water-loving species.

CAUTION In large doses, eucalyptus oil irritates the kidneys and is a powerful depressant of the central nervous system.

HABITAT Native to Tasmania and Australia. Introduced in Central and South America, in California, Africa, India, southern Europe and Ireland.

DESCRIPTION Tall, attractive tree growing to 60m(195ft) or 35m(115ft) in cooler climates. The trunk is smooth and cream coloured with a covering of greyish-blue bark that peels off in narrow strips. The narrow, leathery, sword-shaped leaves have a prominent mid-rib. They are studded with oil glands, are fragrant and greenish-blue in colour. Creamy-white flowers are borne on short flat stalks, followed by fruit that is concealed in an aromatic, camphor-scented, woody cup.

Evening Primrose

Oenothera biennis

Onagraceae
Evening star

The evening primrose clearly acquired its name from the customary evening opening of its flowers, while evening star refers to the pale yellow gleam of the flowers in the fading light. The origin of the botanical name *Oenothera* is unclear. According to certain authorities, it is derived from a Greek word for aperitif, for which purpose the pickled roots were eaten by nineteenth-century Germans.

In the last ten years, evening primrose has been the subject of much scientific investigation, due to the presence of a particular unsaturated fatty acid, gamma lineoleic acid (GLA), in the oil extracted from its seeds. Several clinical trials have taken place to assess the remarkable healing qualities of this substance, which has been shown to have beneficial effects on eczema, psoriasis and acne, and alcohol withdrawal symptoms or hangovers. Current research is being directed at the effectiveness of the oil in multiple sclerosis. GLA is a hormone-like substance that has been particularly successful in bringing relief from such premenstrual discomforts as bloating, sore breasts and mood swings that afflict an estimated 40 per cent of British women. The popularity of evening primrose oil as a home remedy for PMS is evident from the wide range of supplements available at pharmacies and health food stores. In the cosmetic field, evening primrose oil may be found in products for dandruff and for dry, flaky skin.

HABITAT Native to North America. Introduced and naturalized in Europe. Grows on dry, sandy and stony soil on waste ground, railway embankments and sand dunes.

DESCRIPTION Biennial, occasionally annual, with a branched reddish stem growing from 100–130cm(3–4ft). The alternate leaves are lance-shaped and rather hairy. From mid-summer attractive pale lemon-yellow flowers bloom all along the stem and in a spike at the tip. Opening in the early evening, the flowers have four large petals and a subtle fragrance, and are followed by tubular, pointed seed pods.

GROWING TIPS Propagate, preferably from the ripe seed sown in late summer. The plant tolerates most soils but prefers dry, sandy ground and a sunny position. Evening primrose is self-seeding.

Eyebright

Euphrasia officinalis

Scrophulariaceae

Meadow eyebright, *casse-lunettes* (Fr)

As the name suggests, eyebright is a traditional remedy for eye problems, and has been in use since the fourteenth century. The herb's French name, loosely translated as 'throw away your glasses', testifies to its reputation. The botanical name of the plant is derived from the Greek *euphrosyne* meaning gladness, probably due to its sight-preserving qualities. Adherents of the Doctrine of Signatures ensured eyebright's prominence during the sixteenth century. Eyebright's purple-veined white flowers with yellow spots were likened to a bloodshot, diseased eye and so, according to the Doctrine, the plant was designated a cure for eye problems. Culpeper wrote 'If the herb was as much used as it is neglected, it would half spoil the spectacle maker's trade . . .'. Eyebright juice was taken in white wine, as a tea, and even made into an ale. Today, eyebright has maintained its position as the best-known remedy for eyesight, and it is recommended by herbalists where there is a discharge from the eyes, for treating conjunctivitis, and for allergic reactions that affect the eyes. Eyebright also has anti-catarrhal properties and it was once smoked to relieve catarrhal colds and sinusitis.

HABITAT Native European plant, common throughout Britain in meadows, on rough pastureland and heathland. Prefers chalky soils.

DESCRIPTION Small annual to 15cm(6in) with opposite, oval leaves that have scalloped edges. At the top of the stem, spikes of small, white flowers appear from mid-summer to late autumn. The flowers are variable but are usually lipped, veined with purple and flecked with yellow. They are followed by tiny capsules containing many ribbed seeds.

GROWING TIPS Eyebright is difficult to grow as it is a semi-parasitic plant. It feeds off grass and other plants by attaching suckers to the roots and drawing out the nutrients it requires. It will not, however, permanently damage grass.

Fennel

Foeniculum vulgare

Umbelliferae
Wild fennel

Fennel is a corruption of the botanical name *Foeniculum*, itself derived from a Latin word meaning 'little hay' or 'little hair' on account of the strand-like dried leaves. Fennel's culinary use dates back at least 2000 years, and it is the wild ancestor of the bulbous Florence fennel that is so popular in Italian cookery. Wild fennel has a much smaller bulb and tastes bitter in comparison to the cultivated Florentine variety, but the young green stems are said to be edible. It was prized by the Romans for its stems and aromatic seeds. Fennel is mentioned in Anglo-Saxon recipes and was traditionally eaten with salted fish during Lent. This combination fulfilled the dual function of checking flatulence and making the fish more digestible. Florence fennel is still eaten with fish, notably with red mullet, in a traditional Provençal dish known as *grillade au fenouille*.

Medicinally, fennel seed has long been used to expel wind and is popularly taken in the form of a tea. Traditionally offered after such Indian dishes as curries, fennel seed aids the digestion of rich or fatty foods. In the seventeenth century fennel seed acquired a reputation as a slimming aid that still persists today. The seeds were, in fact, commonly chewed to relieve hunger pangs. In many of the old herbals fennel seed was held to strengthen the eyes. Snakes, after shedding their skins, were reputed to eat the plant to revive their eyesight. Fennel has a mildly stimulant effect and was once recommended to increase the flow of milk in nursing mothers.

HABITAT Native to the Mediterranean. Introduced and naturalized in Europe and the USA. Grows on sea cliffs, coast paths and waste ground. Prefers dry soils near the sea.

DESCRIPTION Hardy perennial that resembles dill but is taller and stouter, growing to 1.5m(5ft). The thick, blue-green stems bear aromatic, feathery, fan-shaped leaves with thread-like leaflets. From early summer to early autumn, flat umbels of mustard yellow flowers appear followed by greyish-brown fruits (seeds).

GROWING TIPS Sow the seeds in spring in a sunny position, preferably in a light, well-drained soil. Keep the soil moist after sowing but do not overwater once the plant is in leaf.

Fenugreek

Trigonella foenum-graecum

Papilionaceae
Bird's foot

Fenugreek is an abbreviation of the herb's specific botanical name *foenum graecum*, meaning Greek hay. According to one source, the name reflects fenugreek's use as a fodder plant for animals, while other sources describe the practice of scenting stale or inferior hay with fenugreek. Bird's foot, the plant's common mame, refers to the tri-foliate shape of the leaves, which resembles the structure of a bird's foot. For its culinary and medicinal qualities, fenugreek has been valued since the time of the ancient Greeks, and it was introduced into European medicine before the ninth century by Benedictine monks. The aromatic seed has a slightly bitter celery-like taste and is a common flavouring in curries and chutneys. The young green leaf may also be curried. Fenugreek seed has been roasted in the Middle East as a coffee substitute, and ground, with sesame seed, to make the sweetmeat halva. The seeds are particularly nutritious when sprouted, like alfalfa, and eaten fresh in salads.

Fenugreek seed has acquired something of a reputation as an aphrodisiac, and chemical analysis has revealed the presence of diosgenin, a substance that acts in a similar fashion to the body's own sex hormones. An old remedy for increasing the flow of milk in nursing mothers, fenugreek seed has been recommended by Chinese herbalists for impotence and for restoring hair growth to balding scalps. Fenugreek seed, due to its high mucilage content, has soothing and expectorant properties that are useful in bronchitis. The mashed seeds also make an effective poultice for sores, boils, and skin eruptions.

HABITAT Native to the Mediterranean and western Asia. Naturalized in North America. Widely cultivated in the Middle East, India, and North Africa.

DESCRIPTION Fragrant, erect annual to 50cm(20in) with a round, smooth stem. The leaves are grouped in threes, like clover leaves, but have toothed margins and hairy stalks. In mid-summer white to yellowish pea-like flowers grow from the leaf axils. They are followed by narrow, beaked seed pods, often sickle-shaped, containing between 10 and 20 brown seeds.

GROWING TIPS Fenugreek will thrive in rich, well-drained garden soil. Sow in spring in a sunny position. The seeds reach maturity in four months and are then ready for drying.

Feverfew

Chrysanthemum parthenium or *Tanacetum parthenium*

Compositae

Featherfew, featherfoil

Feverfew, from the Latin *febrifugia* or fever-dispeller, was once a folk remedy for 'ague'. To cure this type of fever, characterized by either sweating or shivering, the fresh leaves were bound around the wrists. Feverfew was also planted around houses to keep out disease. Considered a general tonic by the old herbalists, Culpeper recommended the leaves steeped in wine for 'those troubled with melancholy and heaviness or sadness of spirits'. Today feverfew is no longer prescribed for fevers but has maintained its reputation as a domestic remedy for indigestion, sleeplessness and headaches. In the late 1970s feverfew was subjected to clinical trials following claims that eating the fresh leaves cured migraine attacks. One study found that after taking feverfew, one out of three sufferers had no further migraine attacks, while other trials confirmed feverfew's traditional success in treating indigestion and poor sleeping habits. Some herbalists recommend that migraine sufferers eat small amounts of the bitter-tasting fresh leaf daily as a preventive measure, but warn that certain people may develop mouth ulcers. The herb is thought to ward off attacks by preventing spasms in the blood vessels of the face and head.

Like its relative pyrethrum, feverfew has insecticidal properties. Dabbed on the skin, a solution of feverfew is said to be an effective insect repellant, while a tincture of the herb has relieved painful bites and stings.

HABITAT Native of South-east Europe. Introduced and naturalized elsewhere including the UK, Canada, and North America – from Ohio to Missouri and California. Found on wood edges, walls, hedgerows, roadsides, and waste ground. Cultivated commercially, and a double-flowered variety is grown horticulturally.

DESCRIPTION Perennial plant with branched, hairy stems to 50cm(20in) that are trailing in habit. The fan-shaped, yellow-green leaves have a strong, slightly bitter scent and are deeply lobed. The upper leaves are toothed and segmented. From mid-summer to mid-autumn clusters of daisy-like flowers appear that are similar to chamomile, but smaller and with flat, not conical, centres.

GROWING TIPS Sow the seeds in early spring, preferably indoors in pots or under glass. Thin out and plant in well-drained soil in early summer, preferably in a sunny, sheltered position.

Fig

Ficus carica

Moraceae

In ancient Greece where figs were a staple food, athletes ate the ripe fruit for added stamina. The Romans considered the fig a symbol of plenty, and the leaf is a familar device for preserving the subject's modesty in classical painting and sculpture. Medicinally, the fruit has a mild laxative action and is a popular folk remedy for constipation.

HABITAT Indigenous to western Asia and now found wild in most Mediterranean countries, and widely distributed in Europe, and the UK in sheltered areas.

DESCRIPTION Small tree to 9m(30ft) with a short trunk, branching fairly close to the ground. The smooth bark is pale grey and the dark green leaves have three to five oval lobes. The familiar pear-shaped fruits ripen from green to dark purple, bursting open to reveal the red inner flesh, later darkening to brown.

Figwort

Scrophularia nodosa

Scrophulariaceae

Knotted figwort, scrofula plant

Figwort, as one common name suggests, was used to treat scrofula, a tuberculous disease characterized by glandular swellings, and also prescribed for piles. Today, herbalists value figwort's cleansing properties and recommend it for skin problems, including eczema and psoriasis.

HABITAT Native to Europe and introduced in North America from Maine to Kansas. Common in wet woodland, thickets, and damp, shady places.

DESCRIPTION Strongly scented perennial to 90cm(3ft) on a tuberous rootstock. The stem is dull green, often purplish, with opposite pairs of heart-shaped leaves. From early summer to early autumn, spikes of greenish-brown flowers appear, followed by oval, pointed capsules.

Flax

Linum usitatissimum

Linaceae
Linseed

Flax has been cultivated since 5000 BC for its strong fibre, and is mentioned in the books of Genesis and Exodus. The specific botanical name *usitatissimum*, meaning most useful, reflects the value and varied uses of flax. The stem fibre was principally employed by early societies for making clothing, but was also fashioned into rope, cord, fishing nets, and used to make sails. In Teutonic mythology, the goddess Hulda introduced flax to humankind and taught the art of spinning and weaving. Today, flax is widely grown commercially for the manufacture of linen, notably in Ireland, northern Europe, and the USA.

Poultices for boils and inflammations may be made from the crushed ripe seed of the plant, known as linseed. The seed has good drawing properties and relieves pain and irritation. Infusions of the seed are also soothing, due to their mucilage content, and herbalists may recommend them for chest and lung infections, such as bronchitis and pleurisy. The seed also makes an effective bulk laxative. The light yellow oil obtained from flax seeds, known as linseed oil, was formerly taken to ease the passage of gallstones through the body but is no longer used medicinally. Up until World War II, linseed oil was the basic ingredient of household paints and varnishes. Now it has largely been replaced by synthetic ingredients, although organic paint manufacturers continue to use linseed oil, as do artists who paint in oils. Linseed oil is an ingredient of good-quality furniture polishes, and it is a natural finish for wood. Once most of the oil has been extracted from the seeds, they are made into seed cake and used as cattle fodder.

HABITAT Origin uncertain. Widely distributed in temperate zones and cultivated commercially in northern Europe, north-western USA, and Russia. Found wild only as an escape, on waste ground and roadsides.

DESCRIPTION Graceful, slender annual to 60cm(2ft) with erect stems branching from the base. The narrow, stalkless leaves are lance-shaped and marked with three veins. From early to late summer five-petalled pale blue flowers appear; these are followed by a round pea-size capsule containing shiny brown seeds.

Foxglove

Digitalis purpurea

Scrophulariaceae

Fairies' gloves, dead man's bells

Foxglove's botanical name *Digitalis*, meaning finger, reflects the shape of the plant's flowers. The resemblance to fingers is also echoed in the common names foxglove and fairies' gloves. Foxglove has long been considered the plant of the fairies or good folk, and the name may be a corruption of folk's glove. The white markings inside the flowers are said to be elves' fingerprints. According to another version fairies showed the fox how to muffle his footsteps with the flowers so that he could catch more farmyard chickens on his nightly prowls. All parts of the foxglove are very poisonous, as indicated by another country name, dead man's bells.

Although foxglove had a certain folk reputation for healing sores and easing coughs, it was not until 1785 that foxglove's remarkable medicinal potential was discovered. A traditional domestic remedy for dropsy in the English Midlands region, foxglove tea was studied and analyzed by William Withering who found that a substance contained in the leaves not only strengthened the heartbeat but encouraged the kidneys to eliminate excess fluid, a characteristic of dropsy, from the body. Today, the main active principle of foxglove, digitoxin, is extracted and employed in orthodox medicine as a heart stimulant. Homeopaths may also prescribe minimal doses of the plant for extreme weakness and faintness. Although *Digitalis purpurea* was originally used to extract the glycosides digitoxin and digoxin, supplies are now taken from a related Greek species *Digitalis lanata*.

CAUTION All parts of foxglove are highly toxic. To be used only under medical supervision.

HABITAT Familiar western European wild flower, widespread in the UK and introduced in North America, especially in northern and central states. Common in hedgerows, wood edges, lanes, roadsides and dry meadows on rough, rocky soils. Widely cultivated for pharmaceutical use, and also as a garden ornamental.

DESCRIPTION Biennial, sometimes perennial, from 120cm–2m(4–6ft) producing a long, stout flowering stem in the second year. At the base is a rosette of large, downy grey-green leaves with finely indented margins and stalks. The stem leaves are progressively smaller towards the top, and short stalked. From early summer to mid-autumn the familiar bell-shaped drooping flowers appear. They are crimson to purplish-pink in colour, and the inner surface of the lower lip is mottled with white.

Fringe Tree
Chionanthus virginicus

Oleaceae
Snowdrop tree, old man's beard

Chionanthus, from the Greek for snow flower, reflects the beautiful snowdrop-like flowers of the fringe tree. Herbalists consider the reddish-brown root bark of the tree a valuable bitter tonic for treating liver and gallbladder problems.

HABITAT North American native found in the central states, south to Texas and Florida, and also in New England. Grows in woods and along river banks on rich, moist soil. Cultivated as an ornamental in parks and gardens.

DESCRIPTION Small deciduous tree to 8m(25ft) with smooth, oval leaves similar to those of the magnolia. From late spring when the leaves are not yet fully open, clusters of fragrant and delicate white flowers with fringe-like petals appear. They are followed by oval purple berries.

Fumitory
Fumaria officinalis

Fumariaceae
Earth smoke

Both the common and botanical names of this plant reflect its smoky appearance from a distance. Legend has it that fumitory was formed out of vapours rising from the earth. The plant has long been a traditional remedy for such skin problems as eczema and acne, due to its internal cleansing action.

HABITAT Native to Europe and widely naturalized. Found on roadsides and a common weed in gardens and on cultivated land.

DESCRIPTION Small, slender, densely spreading annual from 15–70cm(6–27in). The grey-green, segmented leaves are fan-shaped. From mid-summer to late autumn, spikes of small pink, tubular flowers appear. Tipped with dark purple, or sometimes white, the upper petal is pouched at the base.

Garlic

Allium sativum

Liliaceae

Garlic is a corruption of two Anglo-Saxon words – *gar*, a lance (from the shape of the stem), and *leac*, a plant. Cultivated since the earliest times, garlic was highly esteemed by the ancient Egyptians who ensured that the slaves building the Great Pyramid at Cheops were given a daily supply. The Romans also acknowledged garlic's strengthening powers and fed it to their soldiers before battle. Garlic was once thought to protect the spirit as well as the body: the ancient Greeks left garlic offerings at crossroads to placate the underworld goddess Hecate, and in modern myth cloves of garlic are reputed to serve as a protection against vampires. Garlic has antibacterial properties that help the immune system to fight infection. It may be taken as a preventative against colds, and was once used successfully to curb the spread of dysentery, diptheria, whooping cough and typhoid. Its antiseptic properties were invaluable in World Wars I and II, when it was used to stop wounds turning septic. Modern research has shown that regular intake of garlic lowers cholesterol levels in the blood, making it particularly useful for coronary-artery disease.

In the Middle Ages, garlic was regarded as a vegetable and eaten with relish. Today, although some dishes call for fairly substantial amounts of garlic, we consider it a flavouring and use it with rather more restraint. The sweetish aroma and characteristic taste of garlic permeate most Mediterranean, Eastern, and South American dishes, and it is fundamental to the classic southern French and Spanish sauce *aioli*. Lovers of raw garlic enjoy its pungent taste in salad dressings and sauces, while cooked garlic is milder in taste and improves the flavour of hundreds of savoury dishes. Counteract garlicky breath by eating fresh parsley or fenugreek seeds.

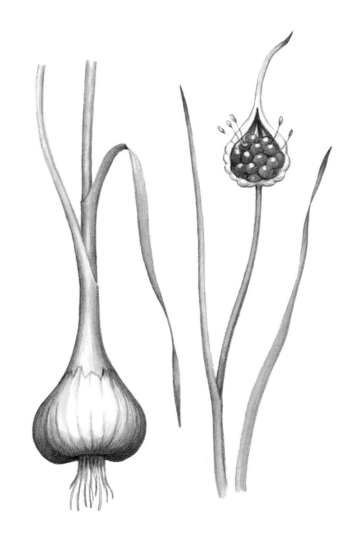

HABITAT Thought to be native to Asia, and possibly southern Siberia. Cultivated in the Mediterranean region for centuries. Introduced to all warm climates.

DESCRIPTION Perennial or biennial member of the onion family with a bulb consisting of several cloves enveloped in a pinkish-white, parchment-like coating. The stem, from 15–30cm(6–12in), is unbranched and bears long, flat, pointed, grass-like leaves that are sheathed at the base. At the tip of the stem a rounded umbel of whitish flowers appears, often interspersed with small bulbs. Before flowering, the umbel is encased in a teardrop-like membrane that tapers to a sharp, green point.

GROWING TIPS Plant individual cloves in early spring to a depth of 5cm(2in) in rich, well-drained soil in a sunny, sheltered position. Lift when the tops have withered.

Gentian, Yellow

Gentiana lutea

Gentianaceae

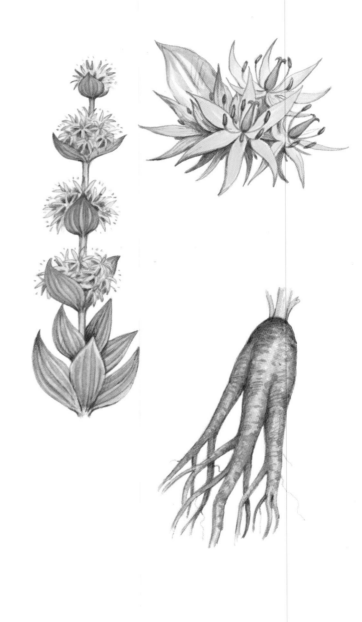

Gentiana, the botanical genus, takes its name from Gentius, an ancient king of Illyria in the first or second century BC who is said to have discovered gentian root's medicinal qualities. Egyptian records, however, show that the plant was used medicinally as early as 1200 BC. The ancient Greeks recommended gentian root for stomach and liver problems and it was thought to offer protection against infectious disease, possibly on account of its unremittingly bitter taste. Gentian's reputation as a guard against infection appears to have persisted into the Middle Ages when it was used to antidote poisons. Gentian root is indeed remarkable for its virtually unrivalled bitterness, and is considered a valuable digestive tonic. It works by stimulating the production of digestive juices and improves both appetite and digestion. Herbalists recommend gentian root for loss of appetite and such digestive problems as dyspepsia and flatulence. Once used as an occasional bitter flavouring in brewing before the introduction of hops, gentian wine was a popular eighteenth-century aperitif. The fermented and distilled root is still a common ingredient of bitter European aperitifs and liqueurs, notably the French drink, *suze*. The flavour of such beverages, however, is considered an acquired taste. Gentian root is lifted in the autumn and dried very slowly to enable the characteristic taste and odour to develop. Its bitterness is not diminished by drying or dilution.

HABITAT Native of Central European Alpine meadows. Widespread in mountainous pastures and on wooded slopes. Cultivated commercially in eastern Europe, and North America.

DESCRIPTION Perennial on a thick yellowish taproot to 30cm(12in). The stem reaches 110cm(43in) and at each joint bears a pair of veined, yellowish-green leaves oval in shape and tapering to a point. In late summer whorls of attractive bright yellow star-shaped flowers appear in the leaf axils of the upper stem.

GROWING TIPS An attractive garden plant, yellow gentian requires a deep loamy or peaty soil and a sunny position with shelter from cold winds. Sow the seeds in spring in a cold frame. Lift the roots in autumn.

Ginger

Zingiber officinale

Zingiberaceae

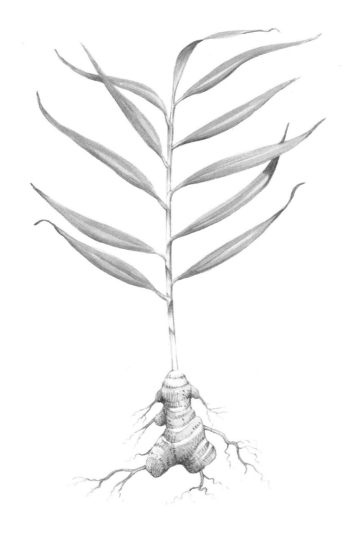

One of the oldest known spices, ginger found its way from the East to southern Europe long before the time of the Roman Empire. In Europe during the Middle Ages, ginger was considered an important food and medicine, and in the sixteenth century the Spanish established ginger cultivation in Jamaica. At first Chinese crystallized ginger and the dried root were principally imported, but now the milder-tasting fresh root is widely available and is ideal for curries and oriental dishes. Fresh ginger keeps well – wrap first in absorbent paper then cover with plastic and store in the fridge. When buying fresh ginger look for plump, knobbly rhizomes with firm, not shrivelled, skin. Ground ginger is widely used in European gingerbreads, biscuits, cakes, puddings and beer. In the grinding process, however, ginger loses some of the volatile essential oil that is responsible for its characteristic taste. Bruising then grinding the dried, whole root gives a better flavour than buying the spice ready ground.

Ginger's warming, aromatic properties have long been used to treat colds and flu. A most important herb in traditional Chinese medicine, ginger is a 'yang' or hot herb that is specific for ailments that are characterized by coldness, and which may be associated with cold, damp weather. Ginger promotes a beneficial sweating that helps to eliminate toxins from the system, and may be taken as a tea with honey and lemon at the first signs of a chill. The fresh or dried root also stimulates the circulation and is helpful for cold hands and feet. Ginger, like many common kitchen spices, aids the digestion of food, and some people like to eat stem ginger as a digestive sweetmeat at the end of a meal. Herbalists value ginger for its calming effect on the digestive system. It is often included in laxative preparations to alleviate any griping pains, and one study found it was beneficial for travel sickness.

HABITAT Probably native to south-east Asia, particularly China. Introduced and cultivated in many other tropical countries including Jamaica, West Africa, India, Australia, and the USA, in southern Florida. Requires shade, rich, well-drained soil, and a tropical climate.

DESCRIPTION Perennial on stout, buff-coloured, aromatic, tuberous rhizome with swollen finger-like joints. In spring the rhizome produces an erect, reed-like stem growing from 60–120cm(2–4ft) with narrow, sword-shaped leaves. The flowering stem produces spikes of fragrant yellowish-white or greenish-white lipped blossoms, streaked with purple.

GROWING TIPS Plant fresh root ginger in a pot and keep it in a warm, moist atmosphere, putting it outside in the shade during hot weather. Harvest the root after 12 months.

Ginseng, Oriental

Panax ginseng or *Panax pseudoginseng*

Araliaceae

Chinese or Korean ginseng

Ginseng, the 'kingly herb' is derived from *Renshen*, a Chinese word meaning man-root, after the curiously human-like root with its two legs. On account of its shape, Chinese herbalists pronounced ginseng a herb of well-being and it was extensively employed in Chinese medicine for centuries. Indeed, wars were fought over the rights to harvest the root and particularly fine specimens were valued more highly than gold. The plant's botanical name, *Panax*, means heal-all in Greek, and is the root of our word panacea. Ginseng seems to have acquired a reputation as a cure-all and many extravagant claims have been made for its powers, from improved memory function to longevity. The root does have an extensive range of beneficial health effects but it is not a cure for every ailment or even for specific ailments. Ginseng works in a more holistic manner by strengthening the whole body so that it can more easily deal with stress and infection. Ginseng has both stimulant and sedative qualities, depending on what the body requires, and it has no demonstrable effects on a healthy system. For these remarkable normalizing powers, ginseng has been classified as an 'adaptogen' by western medicine. This is a substance that increases the body's resistance to stresses, and helps to restore a balanced state of health. Adaptogens adapt to circumstances by working only when the system is unbalanced. In Chinese medicine, ginseng is often combined with other herbs, and may be taken intermittently over a long period to ensure greater well-being in future years. As a tonic, it is particularly beneficial to those weakened by illness or old age. Ginseng also helps the body to cope with such traumas as accidents or surgery. The root was administered to wounded Korean soldiers to sustain them until they could receive medical attention. Modern herbalists advise that ginseng should be treated with respect and taken only in times of stress, as an occasional helper.

Today, ginseng's accepted tonic properties have ensured its wide availability in pharmacies and health food stores. Available in the form of capsules, extracts, teas, and an ingredient of alcohol-free health drinks, ginseng chewing gum is also promised. Pure ginseng root is, however, the most potent form of the herb and, next to wild ginseng, the best quality root comes from Korea. There, ginseng cultivation is a lucrative national industry over which the Korean Government exercises strict control.

HABITAT Native to East Asia, particularly Manchuria in China, and also Korea. Once found wild in cool, damp woods but now extremely rare. Cultivated commercially in China and Korea.

DESCRIPTION Perennial from 60–80cm(24–30in) on an aromatic, branched rootstock that is often forked. The single, erect stem is reddish in colour and produces, near the top, a whorl of three to five ribbed leaves. These are oval in shape with finely serrated edges and taper to a point. From mid to late summer and after three to four years, sparse umbels of greenish-yellow flowers appear at the tip of the stem, followed by bright red berries.

Ginseng, American
Panax quinquefolium

Araliaceae
Five-fingers, five-leafed ginseng

American ginseng contains many, but not all the same active ingredients as oriental ginseng. The Chinese considered it less effective, but at one time they imported large quantities of the wild American root to supplement their own diminishing supplies. Records suggest that trading relations between China and America began as a direct consequence of the correspondence between two Jesuit priests. A Canadian priest living in China sent a sample Chinese root to a fellow Jesuit, Father Lafiteu, in Montreal. This motivated the discovery of wild ginseng in Canada and Father Lafiteu began exporting ginseng to China in 1718. As a source of income, the ginseng trade was exceptionally lucrative until the end of the nineteenth century when the wild root became so scarce that preparations were made for large-scale cultivation. Native American tribes, particularly the Chippewa and Ojibwa, used the root medicinally to relieve nausea, and it was a popular ingredient of love potions.

Cultivated American ginseng is not as potent as the wild plant, and is thought to be weaker than its cultivated oriental relative. Another species, Siberian ginseng (*Eleutherococcus senticosus*), is considered to possess similar properties to oriental ginseng and is less expensive. Russian athletes use the root to aid recuperation following intensive training.

HABITAT Native to cool wooded areas of eastern and central North America, from Quebec and Ontario south to Oklahoma and Alabama. Now thought to be unknown in its wild state. Cultivated commercially, principally in Marathon County, Wisconsin.

DESCRIPTION Similar in appearance to oriental ginseng, but smaller, and with pinkish-coloured flowers. The leaves are more oblong in shape, tapering less, and more abruptly pointed: the margins are coarsely serrated or toothed.

Golden Seal

Hydrastis canadensis

Ranunculaceae

Orange root, eye balm

Golden seal is a celebrated Native American medicinal and dye plant. Modern herbalists value the healing action of the root for inflammation of the digestive system, and it makes a soothing wash for eye infections.

HABITAT Native to Canada and eastern North American states. Once found in shady woods and meadows with rich, moist soil but now rare in the wild.

DESCRIPTION Lòw perennial from 15–30cm(6–12in) on a thick, twisted, horizontal rhizome that is bright yellow inside. In early spring at the top of the hairy flowering stem two large, prominently-veined, five-lobed leaves appear. From late spring the plant produces a solitary greenish-white flower without petals, followed by a raspberry-like fruit.

Goldenrod

Solidago virgaurea

Compositae

Woundwort, European goldenrod

Solidago is from the Latin verb, to make whole, and reflects goldenrod's old reputation as a wound-healer. Today European herbalists employ goldenrod's antiseptic, diuretic properties for treating urinary infections.

HABITAT Native to Europe, northern and western Asia. Grows on heathland, grassland, dry banks and cliffs.

DESCRIPTION Erect perennial to 1m(3ft) with sparsely branched stems and oval, pointed leaves with very slightly toothed margins. From late summer to autumn, spikes of daisy-like golden flowers appear towards the end of the stem.

Hawthorn

Crataegus oxyacantha or *Crataegus monogyna*

Rosaceae

May blossom, bread and cheese

May blossom reflects the hawthorn's traditional flowering time, and the Mayflower, the Pilgrim Fathers' ship, took its name from this tree. Schoolchildren in rural England used to nibble the sweet young leaf buds, which they called bread and cheese. Haw is an old word for hedge or enclosure, and clipped hawthorns became the most common hedging plant in England during the nineteenth-century land enclosures. According to Christian legend, the crown of thorns was made from hawthorn and the famous Glastonbury thorn in southern England sprouted from the staff of Joseph of Aramathea. Superstitions also surround this small tree: witches were said to shelter in hawthorn hedges, and to cut the wood down would bring either fairies or bad luck into the house. In earlier times, however, the hawthorn was regarded more kindly and associated with lovers, possibly due to the strong musky scent of the flowers which attracts pollinating insects. The ancient Greeks and Romans considered its blossom a symbol of joy and hope, and made it into wedding bouquets. Paradoxically, considering the tree's later associations, the leaves were also brought into Roman homes to protect new babies from evil spirits.

Hawthorn is particularly valued for its strengthening and normalizing effect on the heart. In medical studies and research work, the berries lowered blood pressure by helping to dilate clogged and hardened arteries. The flowers help to strengthen weak or ageing hearts. Hawthorn also eases the painful chest-constriction characteristic of angina, and can help to regularize an erratic heartbeat. In Germany, hawthorn extract is the active ingredient of some medications.

In winter, hawthorn berries were gathered to make a warming brandy, while the fine-grained wood was used as fuel and made into small articles such as boxes and combs. In spring, hawthorn-blossom liqueur may be made by steeping the flowers in brandy.

HABITAT Small native European tree. Introduced into other temperate zones, including the USA. Found on heathland, chalk downs, and in open deciduous woods. Widespread in hedges, along roadsides, and field boundaries. Grown as an ornamental in parks and gardens.

DESCRIPTION Shrub or small tree from 4.5–9m(15–29ft) with greyish bark and tough, thorny branches, often gnarled. The small, dark green leaves are shiny and have three lobes. From May to June, clusters of small creamy white flowers with red anthers and often tinged with pink, appear. They are followed by deep scarlet berries.

Hemlock

Conium maculatum

Umbelliferae

Poison parsley

Conium, hemlock's botanical name, is derived from a Greek verb that means to whirl around. This refers to the vertigo that is one of the characteristic symptoms of hemlock poisoning. The entire plant contains a deadly poisonous juice that has proved fatal in cases where the leaves were mistaken for wild parsley or the root for wild parsnip. The ancient Greeks were well acquainted with the effects of hemlock juice. Reputed to be the principal ingredient in the poisoned brew that Socrates was forced to swallow, hemlock was a favourite drink of suicides, and was also administered to criminals who were condemned to death on the orders of the state of Athens. This sinister plant was held to be a favourite of witches who gathered it for their noxious brews, and in Russian and German folklore it was known as the devil's plant.

Despite its poisonous nature and 'loathsome smell', hemlock was first used medicinally by Greek and Arabian physicians. Dioscorides prescribed the herb for the external treatment of herpes, and a poultice was once applied to tumours. The poisons were said to dissipate on cutting and drying, and Culpeper recommended the roasted and wrapped root to ease the pain and swelling of gout. Hemlock was investigated medicinally in the latter part of the eighteenth century and continued to be administered to cancerous swellings and ulcers. In the early part of this century, hemlock was listed in the British, Indian and North American Pharmacopeias as a sedative and antispasmodic drug, and prescribed for epilepsy and other convulsive diseases. Hemlock was also considered an effective antidote to strychnine poisoning. Today, hemlock is no longer employed medicinally due to the considerable variation in the strength of the herb, and the unpredictability of its effect.

CAUTION All parts of the fresh plant are intensely poisonous.

HABITAT Native to southern and central Europe and widespread in temperate zones. Common in damp hedgerows, stream banks, moist, rough pastureland and on waste ground.

DESCRIPTION Tall biennial similar to cow parsley and wild chervil, and growing to 2m(6ft) from a forked, pale yellow root. The stout, bright green stem is smooth and blotched with purple or deep red, and the delicate, dark green leaves are feathery and grouped in threes. The leaves have an unpleasant, 'mousy' smell when bruised. From mid-summer to mid-autumn, umbels of small white, lacy flowers appear, followed by seeds (fruits) that resemble caraway.

Henbane

Hyoscyamus niger

Solanaceae

Stinking nightshade, hog's bean

Poisonous henbane has been considered an important medicinal herb for at least 2000 years due to the valuable sedative, pain-killing, and muscle-relaxing properties of the leaves. In the first century AD, Dioscorides used henbane as a sleeping potion and pain killer, while during the Middle Ages henbane seeds were smoked as a home remedy for toothache and rheumatic pain. The results of this home cure proved unpredictable and instances of delirium, convulsions and insanity were recorded. Gerard wrote that the herb caused 'an unquiet sleep, like unto the sleep of drunkeness, which continueth long and is deadly to the patient'. Culpeper declared henbane to be under the dominion of the planet Saturn, ruler of the bones and skeleton, and prescribed the leaves for pains in the joints, sciatica and headaches. Henbane was formerly an official sedative and analgesic that was prescribed for painful muscular spasms of the urinary tract, for asthma, and for hysteria. Successive small-doses were also given for insomnia, neuralgia, and nervous headache. Today henbane is only rarely employed internally as a medicine because of the risk of poisoning.

Henbane was reputed to be a principal ingredient of witches' brews and sorcerers' ointments. It was widely employed in magical and satanic rites for its power to provoke hallucinations and convulsions, and smoked as a tobacco for its narcotic effects, often with dangerous consequences. In 1910, the famous British murderer Dr Crippen poisoned his wife with henbane. Pigs, however, were reputed to suffer no ill effects from eating the herb, hence the name hog's bean.

CAUTION All parts of this plant are poisonous.

HABITAT Native to Europe. Introduced to Canada and northern USA, western Asia, and parts of South America. Grows wild on waste ground, in sandy places near the sea, and around derelict buildings and rubbish heaps.

DESCRIPTION Annual or biennial from 30–75cm(12–30in) with a powerful, nauseating smell. At the base of the stem the dull grey-green leaves are flat, oblong and coarsely indented; higher up the leaves are prominently veined, stalkless and a paler green. Both stem and leaves are sticky to the touch. From early to late summer, dull, buff-coloured, funnel-shaped flowers appear that are hairy and marked with lurid purple veins. The lids of the enclosed, bean-like seed capsules that follow split open to reveal numerous small seeds.

Henna

Lawsonia inermis

Lythraceae

Egyptian privet

Henna comes from the Arabic word, *Al Kenna*. For around 5000 years, the rich red pigment from the leaves of the henna shrub has been used to dye hair, hands, feet and nails. Henna was widely used as a cosmetic in ancient Egypt and examination of mummified remains from the tombs of ancient Egyptians has revealed that a mixture of henna and indigo, called 'reng', was used to colour hair and false beards. In the East, henna's redness symbolized the fiery energy and life-blood of the earth that connects humankind to nature. Painting the body with henna, therefore, demonstrates a connection with natural processes and cycles, such as birth, death and conception. It is still the custom among certain orthodox Muslim and Hindu women to gather together to paint the bride's hands and feet with henna patterns on the eve of a marriage ceremony. Muslim men also use henna to colour their beards. In North Africa it is still traditional amongst some Berbers to colour the skin of new babies and embalm corpses with henna. Today, a growing reaction against the potentially damaging or allergenic chemicals in synthetic hair colourings has provoked a revival of natural herbal hair colours. Powdered henna leaf produces a lovely shine and a rich red tone that fades naturally and will not harm the hair or scalp. The colour can be varied and darkened by mixing it with such dye plants as indigo, lucerne and catechu. Adding other common kitchen ingredients such as coffee, vinegar or red wine further modifies the colour. The best quality henna is said to come from Iran, and the young shoots produce the finest deep red tones. Egyptian henna produces a more orange-red effect.

Medicinally, powdered henna leaf has an astringent action and was once used externally to treat leprosy, smallpox and other skin diseases. Today, henna is rarely used medicinally.

HABITAT Native to Arabian countries, Iran, India and Egypt. Introduced and naturalized in North Africa and topical parts of America. Cultivated for cosmetic use principally in Iran, Egypt and Morocco, and also grown as a garden ornamental.

DESCRIPTION Small shrub to 3m(10ft) with oblong or elliptical brownish-green leaves that resemble those of the privet. In summer, heavily perfumed white or red flowers bloom in broad, flattish clusters, followed by round berries.

Hops

Humulus lupulus

Cannabinaceae

Hop bine

Hops, named from an Anglo-Saxon word meaning to climb, became an important flavouring for beer in ninth-century Europe. In the UK, however, the inhabitants preferred traditional ales made from malt flavoured with such herbs as costmary or wormwood. Hops were deemed 'a wicked weed that would spoil the taste of the drink and endanger the people' and it was not until the seventeenth century that the beer brewed from them was as widely available as ale. Following the introduction of hops into Massachusetts in the early part of the seventeenth century, New York State established itself as the principal hop-growing area of North America, maintaining its position until the 1920s. Brewers added hops to their beer primarily because they extended its keeping qualities, although many maintained that their bitterness also improved the flavour.

In the late seventeenth century hops were considered by some to be injurious to health, but the digestive and sedative qualities of the female flowers were soon appreciated by practising herbalists. Hops contain a volatile oil and a bitter principle that have a soothing effect on the central nervous system, and are beneficial for tension and anxiety. Many people report improved sleeping habits after using a pillow stuffed with dried hops. Hops also act as a tonic to the digestive system, relaxing the bowel and easing nervous indigestion. Hops also contain hormonal substances that, taken in large quantities, may be connected with temporary impairment of the male sexual function. After prolonged contact with the flowers, female hop-pickers have been known to suffer interruptions of the menstrual cycle. Hops also possess antiseptic properties and some herbalists recommend external applications of a hot hop poultice to reduce inflammation.

CAUTION Hops depress the central nervous system and should be avoided by those suffering from depression.

HABITAT Native to northern temperate zones, expecially northern Europe, mountainous areas of southern Europe, and the UK. Introduced and cultivated in North America. Widespread commercial cultivation in northern Europe. Grows wild in damp hedgerows and thickets, on humus-rich soils in sheltered situations.

DESCRIPTION Well-known twinning, perennial vine with rough stems that climb to 6m(20ft). The long-stalked leaves with coarsely serrated margins are opposite and deeply indented. They are usually divided into three oval lobes that taper to a point. Yellowish-green flowers appear from late summer to mid-autumn: the female flowers are enclosed in cone-shaped catkins, and the male flowers hang in loose bunches. The ripened female cones (fruits) are used for brewing beer.

Horse Chestnut

Aesculus hippocastanum

Hippocastanaceae

Herbalists employ the inedible fruits of this tree for their strengthening and toning action on the veins. Externally, horse chestnut ointment is considered an effective treatment for haemorrhoids.

HABITAT Native to mountainous areas of Greece and Albania. Introduced and widely cultivated in Europe, the UK and North America.

DESCRIPTION Deciduous tree to 35m(120ft) with stout trunk, greyish bark and spreading branches. The finely toothed, bright-green leaves are grouped in fives, like fingers. In spring the sticky buds burst into erect cones or 'candles' of beautiful pinkish-white flowers. These are followed by globular, spiny, light green capsules containing a highly polished brown fruit.

Horseradish

Cochlearia amoracia or *Amoracia rusticana*

Cruciferae

Red cole

In Medieval England the principal use of horseradish was medicinal: later, following the example of the Germans, the sharp-flavoured pounded root was eaten as a relish with meat and fish. Taken internally, horseradish is a strong diuretic that is traditionally used to treat kidney problems. Externally, a fresh horseradish poultice stimulates the circulation and is a traditional home remedy for rheumatic joints and chilblains.

HABITAT Probably native to south-eastern Europe. Widely cultivated in northern Europe and North America. May be found wild on banks and roadsides.

DESCRIPTION Perennial to 1m(3ft) with a thick, white tapering taproot. The large, stalked leaves resemble those of the dock but are shiny, lighter green and less tough. The margins are dentate and wavy. Clusters of small white flowers appear from mid-summer to mid-autumn.

Horsetail

Equisetum arvense

Equisetaceae

Bottle brush, shave grass

Horsetail's botanical name is derived from two Latin words. *equus* and *seta*, meaning horse and tail respectively. Its common names refer to the tail, or brush-like appearance of the bristly stems. The horsetails comprise a distinct class of plants but have some similarities with ferns. They are thought to have evolved very little since prehistoric times, except in terms of size. The horsetail resembles a miniature tree and, 200 millenia ago, was considerably taller. It may have been one of the dominant plant species of prehistoric Earth.

Horsetail is rich in silica and in Medieval times the stems were used to polish metal, hence the plant's old name pewterwort, as well as to sand and polish wood. Centuries later, dairy maids were using the dried stems to scour their milk pails. Horsetail's high silica content also made it a valuable medicinal plant: the silica has a healing effect on damaged lung tissue and was recommended for lung problems, including mild tuberculosis. The fresh sterile stems are rich in minerals, while the silica helps the body to absorb calcium. Herbalists recommend horsetail for its strengthening effect on thin, lifeless hair and for nails that are brittle or have white spots. A potent and versatile herb, horsetail has mild diuretic and astringent properties that are beneficial for urinary problems such as gravel, enlarged prostate and cystitis. Its astringency in particular is helpful externally for healing wounds and ulcers.

Equisetum hymale, a giant form of horsetail, can reach 1.5m(5ft). It has a tall, ridged stalk but no leaves.

HABITAT Native to Europe and introduced to North America and other temperate regions around the world, with the exception of Australia and New Zealand. Widespread in moist meadows, on waste ground, and in sandy soils near water.

DESCRIPTION Perennial with two types of hollow stem. A fertile, pinkish stem appears first, growing to 20cm(8in) and producing a conical spike that sheds its spores and dies down. Yellowish-green sterile shoots then appear that reach 80cm(32in) and have thread-like, feathery branches growing from the stem joints.

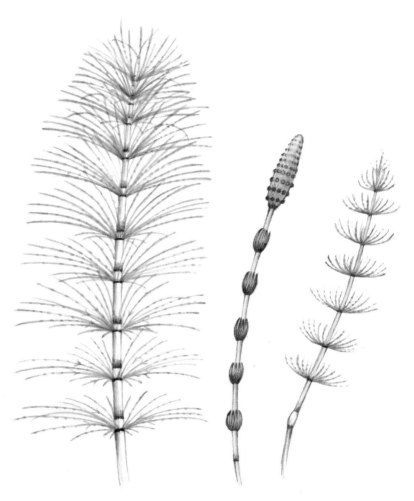

GROWING TIPS Horsetail is rarely cutivated as, once established, it is very difficult to eradicate. It may, however, be prevented from spreading by planting it in containers filled with humus-rich, moist soil.

Hyssop
Hyssopus officinalis
Labiatae

Hyssop has a strong, sharp taste and was a popular flavouring for meats and stews during the Middle Ages. In the home, the aromatic stems were strewn over floors to freshen the air. Hyssop is rarely used in today's kitchen but maintains its reputation as a valuable medicinal herb. Syrup of hyssop is a traditional remedy for chest complaints, catarrh and sore throats. Externally, a hyssop poultice or infusion is recommended for bruising.

HABITAT Native to central and southern Europe and Russia. Introduced and naturalized in North America. Grows wild on dry soils that are rocky or chalky.

DESCRIPTION Hardy, camphor-scented bushy herb or small shrub with branched, square stems to 60cm(2ft). The small, linear leaves are stalkless and grow in whorls at intervals along the stem. From early summer to early autumn, pretty royal blue, white, or pink flowers bloom in the leaf axils, forming dense spikes towards the top of the stem.

Iceland Moss
Cetraria islandica
Parmeliaceae
Iceland lichen

Iceland moss is a wild, starchy foodstuff with soothing and antibiotic properties. The lichen was once used in the treatment of such lung problems as TB, and herbalists still recommend it for bronchitis and catarrh.

HABITAT Widespread in cool, mountainous northern regions including North America, the UK, northern and central Europe. Grows in cool, damp forests on stony ground.

DESCRIPTION Leafy lichen with branched, curly frond (thallus) from 3–12cm(1–5in). The colour varies from greenish brown to grey, and the underside is paler and flecked with white.

Iris, Florentine

Iris florentina or *Iris germanica*

Iridaceae

Orris, white flower de luce

In Greek mythology Iris was the goddess of the many-coloured rainbow. Her name was chosen for this family of plants to reflect the variable colours of their flowers. The iris became the emblem of several French monarchs including Charlemagne and Louis VII and IX, and became known as the fleur de luce or fleur de lys – a corruption of fleur de Louis. The white Florentine iris was first cultivated in the Italian city of Florence during the Middle Ages, and the flower may still be seen on the city's old heraldic arms. The value of this species of iris lay in the pronounced violet scent that developed when the rootstock was dried. The root, commonly available in powdered form, became known as orris, a corruption of iris. Orris has been used as a perfume since the days of the ancient Egyptians. In the late fifteenth century a mixture of powdered anise and orris was used to perfume household linen, while in the eighteenth century sweet-scented orris was a principal ingredient of the cosmetic hair powders that were necessary to maintain the ornate hairstyles of the day.

Orris root contains a volatile oil that acts as a valuable fixative in perfumery and stabilizes the fragrance of pot-pourris. Powdered orris root makes an excellent dry shampoo and may be used as a talcum powder.

Orris root was once employed medicinally for chest problems, and the juice was considered an effective, if rather violent, purgative. Today orris is rarely used medicinally.

HABITAT Native of southern Europe, especially Italy, and naturalized in central Europe, Iran and northern India. Grows wild on hilly slopes in sunny situations. Cultivated commercially, particularly in Italy.

DESCRIPTION Perennial on a thick rhizome with an erect flowering stem to 60cm(2ft), and characteristic sword-shaped leaves. The large flowers usually appear in pairs at the end of the stem from early to mid-summer, and have no scent. The petals are either white with a pale lilac tinge and a yellow 'beard' or pure white.

GROWING TIPS Propagate by root division and plant in late spring or early autumn in deep, rich soil that does not retain moisture. The plant will not tolerate heavy clay soils and requires a warm, sheltered position.

Irish Moss

Chondrus crispus

Rhodophyta

Carrageenan

Irish moss contains a high proportion of mucilage that forms a gel when the dried plant is soaked. Herbalists consider this gel soothing to irritated tissue and prescribe it for coughs, bronchitis and ulcers. Irish moss is traditionally boiled with milk and sweetened to make a nourishing, easily digested food.

HABITAT Widespread on the coastlines of north western Europe, especially the Atlantic coast of Ireland. Collected at low tide, principally in Ireland and northern France.

DESCRIPTION Seaweed, from 10–30cm(4–12in), that varies in colour when fresh from greenish yellow to brown. The fronds are flattened and curled, and turn a translucent yellow or whitish shade when dry. Small oval sacs (fruiting bodies) appear on the stems.

Jasmine

Jasminum officinale

Oleaceae

Common white jasmine, jessamine

In the nineteenth century jasmine blossom was made into a soothing cough syrup. Today, aromatherapists recommend jasmine oil for its calming properties and a strong infusion of the flowers may be added to the water for a relaxing bath. Garlands of jasmine blossoms are traditionally presented as welcoming or parting gifts in India.

HABITAT Native to North India and Iran. Naturalized in central and southern Europe. Cultivated horticulturally in the USA and southern parts of the UK.

DESCRIPTION Vine-like plant with weak stems, climbing to 3.6m(12ft) when supported. The dark green leaves are small, opposite and composed of seven leaflets. The small, highly scented white flowers bloom from early summer to early autumn, filling the air with their fragrant perfume.

Jimson Weed

Datura stramonium

Solanaceae

Thornapple, mad apple, devil's apple

According to some sources, the high priestess of Apollo's oracle at Delphi uttered her strange prophecies under the influence of Jimson weed smoke. The plant has a powerfully narcotic effect, producing hallucinations and double vision. Under the guidance of the shaman, jimson weed was employed in puberty rites and other sacred rituals of south-western Native American tribes. The name of the herb is thought to be a corruption of Jamestown, then a colonial outpost in Virginia. According to one story, a British military detachment bound for Jamestown wandered around in a demented state after inadvertently eating some leaves and never arrived at their destination. Early American settlers considered Jimson weed a dangerous plant and it became known as mad apple or the devil's apple. People even kept it out of their gardens because of its power to summon witches. The witches, however, appreciated the strange flying sensations it produced.

   Jimson weed is a poisonous plant with a strongly narcotic effect, similar to belladonna. Like belladonna, it is also a valuable medicine in precise dosage. The leaves and seeds contain alkaloids that have a marked sedative effect on the central nervous system and a strong action on the respiratory organs. Medicinally, Jimson weed was introduced into Europe in the sixteenth century and by the middle of the eighteenth century the herb was in wide medicinal usage for controlling muscular spasms. The leaves were made into a tobacco and smoked to give relief during asthma attacks, and their sedative effect was useful for controlling the spasms characteristic of Parkinson's disease. The plant was also applied externally or made into an ointment to relieve rheumatic pains and neuralgia. In South America, Jimson weed was considered an aphrodisiac and smoked for its hallucinogenic effects.

CAUTION All parts of the plant, especially the seeds, are poisonous.

HABITAT Probably native to Asia. Naturalized and widespread in North and South America, and throughout Europe. Uncommon in the UK. A familiar weed on waste ground, roadsides, in ditches, and field edges. Grows better in sunny situations.

DESCRIPTION Foul-smelling plant with an erect, rubbery yellow green stem from 1–1.5m(3–5ft) and spreading branches. The leaves are large, dark green and jagged. The upper surface is smooth, veined, and dark green; the underside is paler green. Throughout the summer large, white to pale blue trumpet-shaped flowers appear, followed by green, spiny seed capsules that are oval in shape and burst open to reveal numerous dark brown seeds.

Juniper

Juniperus communis

Cupressaceae

The name juniper is derived from the Dutch word for gin, *jenever*, which was invented in Holland, and formerly known as geneva. Gin owes its characteristic flavour to juniper's volatile oil: once gin distillers added hand-picked berries to the spirit but now they use commercially-produced distilled oil. In regions where juniper is plentiful, the crushed, ripe berries are added to marinades for game birds, cooked with roast meats, and used to flavour pâtés.

Juniper is an important medicinal plant that has been employed since the time of the ancient Greek and Arabian physicians. In common with many other strongly scented and cleansing herbs, juniper was thought to keep out evil spirits as well as disease. In the Middle Ages, a juniper bush was commonly planted by cottage doors as a protection against witches. If, however, the witch could bring herself to count all the needles on the bush then she was permitted to cross the threshhold. Native Americans considered juniper a cleansing herb that would guard against infection.

Juniper berries contain a volatile oil that is both antiseptic and a strong diuretic. Juniper stimulates the kidneys and flushes out the system, so it particularly beneficial for such urinary infections as cystitis, as well as for urethritis and gout. Ripe juniper berries also have a digestive effect and may be taken for colic, while their cleansing action heals infected gums and sweetens the breath. Externally, diluted oil of juniper eases aching muscles and rheumatic and arthritic pain. Aromatherapists recommend the oil for fluid retention and cellulite, and both herbalists and aromatherapists consider steam inhalations of juniper beneficial for relieving catarrh and congestion in coughs and colds.

CAUTION Avoid juniper if you are pregnant or if you suffer from kidney problems.

HABITAT Native to Europe. Extensively distributed worldwide from Russia through Europe and across to North America, growing wild from the Arctic Circle southwards. Found abundantly on mountain slopes, in open coniferous woodland, on heathland and moorland. Prefers dry, rocky ground but will tolerate moist, peaty soils.

DESCRIPTION Variable prickly evergreen occurring as a low, spreading shrub to 1m(3ft) or a small tree to 6m(20ft). The leaves resemble those of other coniferous trees and are flattened into very sharp needles that occur in whorls of three. The upper surface of the leaves is grey-green to grey-blue. From late spring, male and female flowers appear on separate trees. The male flowers are yellow and do not ripen. The female flowers are tiny greenish cones that can take from two to three years to ripen into blue-black fleshy berries.

Lady's Bedstraw

Galium verum

Rubiaceae

Our Lady's bedstraw, cheese rennet

When dried, the flowering stems of lady's bedstraw give off a sweet, hay-like scent. It was a popular strewing herb and mattress stuffing during the Middle Ages, and legend has it that Mary used the stems for Christ's bedding. Sleeping on a pillow stuffed with lady's bedstraw is said to promote sound sleep.

HABITAT Native to Europe. Naturalized in southern Canada, northern and eastern USA, and coastal regions of the UK. Grows in dry, sandy pastures, banks and roadsides.

DESCRIPTION Perennial with slender, erect or creeping stems from 20–80cm(8–32in) that bear whorls of six to eight narrow, thread-like leaves. From early to late summer honey-scented bright yellow flowers appear in terminal spikes.

Lady's Mantle

Alchemilla vulgaris

Rosaceae

Lion's foot

In the Middle Ages alchemists made potions with the overnight dewdrops that collected in the cupped folds of lady's mantle's foliage. The leaves were also likened to the scalloped edge of a cloak, hence the common name. Herbalists employ the astringent leaves to check profuse menstruation.

HABITAT Native to northern Europe and at higher altitudes in central and southern Europe. Found in open woods and grassland.

DESCRIPTION Graceful, entirely green plant to 30cm(12in) covered with fine hairs. The lower leaves are large, kidney-shaped and have seven to nine lobes with toothed edges. Loose clusters of yellow-green flowers bloom from early spring to early autumn.

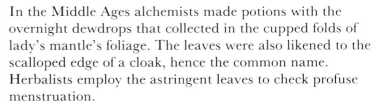

Lavender

Lavandula officinalis or *Lavandula angustifolia*

Labiatae

English lavender

Lavender has always been one of the most popular of all the traditional herbs. Both the common and botanical names of the many species of lavender are probably derived from the Latin verb *lavare* meaning to wash, after the practice of scenting bath and washing water with lavender. Lavender was well known to the ancient Greeks, Romans and Arabs and its fragrance was highly esteemed. According to a Christian legend, the plant acquired its scent from the newly washed clothes of the infant Christ that were hung over a lavender bush to dry. Lavender was a popular cosmetic and strewing herb as early as the twelfth century, and was first cultivated in England after the middle of the sixteenth century. Lavender was among the garden flowers that the Pilgrim Fathers carried with them to America.

Lavender flowers contain a volatile oil that was traditionally inhaled or applied, diluted, to the temples to prevent faintness and 'giddiness or turning of the brain', according to Culpeper. The herb has soothing and sedative properties that are helpful for nervous headaches and tension, and aromatherapists recommend the oil for sleeplessness. Lavender oil has a strong antiseptic action capable of killing the bacteria that carry diphtheria and typhoid. An antiseptic lotion of the herb may be applied to cuts, and it was used to disinfect wounds up until World War I. Lavender is particularly recommended for burns and scalds and can, if applied directly, prevent blistering of the skin. Both flowers and oil have insect repellant properties and are traditionally made into sachets for cupboards and drawers to protect and perfume clothes and bed linen. Soaking a cotton wool ball with lavender oil will deter moths and rubbing the skin with diluted oil makes an effective mosquito repellant.

HABITAT Native to the Mediterranean region and widely distributed in southern Europe. Naturalized in the southern USA and introduced elsewhere. Found on stony, well-drained soils in sunny situations. Widely cultivated commercially, especially in southern France and in the UK. Extensively grown as a garden plant.

DESCRIPTION Bushy, very fragrant perennial with short woody stems to 80cm(32in). The leaves are grey-green to silver-grey in colour. They are narrow, linear and covered with a layer of soft white hairs. From mid-summer to early autumn whorls of six to ten sweet-smelling mauve or pale lilac flowers appear in spikes at the end of long stalks.

GROWING TIPS Propagate from cuttings taken in summer and start in cold frames. Transplant to light, stony soil in a sunny, sheltered position and protect from frost.

Lemon

Citrus limonum

Rutaceae

Lemon is derived from a Hindustani word that was translated into Arabic as *limun*. The fruit is widely used in cooking for its sharpness, and in the cosmetics industry for its astringency. Hot lemon juice is a traditional household remedy for colds and sore throats: the fresh fruit is mildly antiseptic and a good source of Vitamin C. Lemon juice has mild bleaching properties.

HABITAT Probably native to northern India or south-east Asia. Introduced and widely cultivated in Mediterranean countries, California and Florida.

DESCRIPTION Small tree from 3–6m(10–20ft) with greyish bark and stout spines. The pale green leaves are oval and in the axils grow five-petalled flowers that are white inside and pink-tinged outside. They are followed by the well-known sour, yellow fruit.

Lettuce

Lactuca virosa

Compositae

Wild lettuce, prickly lettuce

A wild relative of the garden lettuce, the plant was cultivated in nineteenth century Europe for its juice or latex. The dried latex, known as 'lettuce opium', was employed medicinally in cough mixtures, and, like opium, has mild sedative properties that are useful for restlessness and insomnia.

HABITAT Native European plant that grows on banks and waste ground in dry soils.

DESCRIPTION Biennial with a strong odour that grows to 1.5m(5ft) with a rosette of oblong, rounded leaves and a stout stem that is pale green, branched, and often prickly towards the base. The dark green stem leaves are smaller. From mid-summer to mid-autumn, numerous pale yellow flowers appear. The cut plant exudes a milky juice.

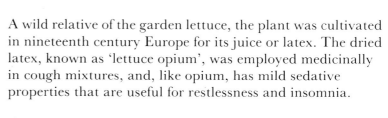

Lily of the Valley

Convallaria majalis

Liliaceae

May lily

Majalis, lily of the valley's specific botanical name, means belonging to May, the traditional flowering time of the plant. Lily of the valley, despite its name, does not grow exclusively in valleys, although it may be found in some wooded alpine valleys. In German folklore, the plant was said to have sprouted beneath the Cross on ground that Mary had watered with her tears. According to English legend, the lily of the valley first appeared in a wooded area in the south-east where St Leonard fought and killed a dragon. Where the saint's blood fell, the flowers bloomed.

Lily of the valley was used medicinally as early as the fourth century. In Russian folk medicine, the plant was a traditional remedy for dropsy caused by a weak heart, and Gerard recommended the distilled flower water for gout. In modern herbalism, lily of the valley, like foxglove, contains substances that have a tonic effect on the heart and can normalize a weak or too-rapid heartbeat. Lily of the valley also acts as a diuretic and helps the body to rid itself of the excess fluids characteristic of dropsy and gout. The dried flowers were once made into a powder and taken like snuff to relieve headaches.

CAUTION The berries are poisonous and the plant must only be used as directed by a qualified practitioner.

HABITAT Native to Europe and eastern Asia and introduced in North America. Rare in the wild in the UK and may be found as an escape in the USA in dry woodland, especially ash woods. Introduced elsewhere and widely cultivated as a garden plant.

DESCRIPTION Very fragrant perennial from 10–20cm(4–8in) that bears a pair of wide, oval prominently ribbed leaves. They are mid- to dark green in colour and taper to a point. From late spring to early summer pretty pearl-white flowers hang down from the stem; they resemble small bells with scalloped edges, and smell very sweet. They are followed by red berries containing seeds.

GROWING TIPS Sow seed in moist, chalky soil under trees or in semi-shade. Propagate by root division in autumn. The plant spreads rapidly.

Lime

Tilia europea

Tiliaceae

Common lime, linden

The common name of lime, linden, is from the German *lind*. The dried, honey-scented flowers make one of the best-known and most pleasant-tasting herbal teas that is commonly served throughout Europe. This tisane is especially popular in France where it is known as *tilleul*, from the Latin name of the tree. In the USA, a similar delicately flavoured beverage known as Basswood tea is made from the dried flowers of a related species, *Tilia americana*. The flowers also produce an excellent honey.

Lime tea is traditionally drunk as a digestive or, like chamomile, as an after-dinner drink to induce a peaceful night's sleep. The flowers have long been used in folk medicine to soothe anxiety and were considered helpful for hysteria, either taken as a tea or added to the bath water. During World War II, lime tea was prescribed for its mildly tranquillizing effect. In Eastern Europe, lime flowers are a traditional remedy for high blood pressure, and they may be used to treat hypertension in combination with hawthorn and mistletoe. Modern herbalists value the calming properties of lime blossom and recommend it for nervous tension and insomnia. In France the tea is considered helpful for soothing excitable and overactive children. Lime flowers also promote sweating and are prescribed for feverish colds and flu, often in combination with elder flowers.

Tilia europea is considered a hybrid between the Broad-leaved lime (*Tilia platyphyllos*) and the Small-leaved lime (*Tilia cordata*). The flowers of all three species possess similar properties.

HABITAT Native to Europe, especially France. Grows in deciduous or mixed woodland on sandy soils and has been widely planted in parks, gardens, and along town streets and city avenues.

DESCRIPTION Large, domed deciduous tree to 25m(81ft) that is very fragrant when in blossom. The finely toothed leaves are heart-shaped and taper to a sharp point. The upper surface is dark green and the undersides are paler. From mid- to late summer sweet-scented yellowish flowers with wing-shaped bracts hang in clusters from the branches. They are followed by small globular fruits.

Liquorice

Glycyrrhiza glabra

Leguminosae

Spanish

Herbalists have been using liquorice to soothe chest and throat complaints since the third century BC. Extract of the sweet-tasting root is also included in cough preparations and widely used to flavour tobacco. English liquorice cultivation was started in Yorkshire by the Dominican Black friars.

HABITAT Native to southern Europe, and from the Middle East to Russia. Grows wild in the rich soil of river valleys, or on sandy soils. Widely cultivated in its native countries and also in California and Arizona.

DESCRIPTION Shrubby perennial from 50–150cm(20–60in) on a vertical, woody taproot that is yellow internally and sends out horizontal stolons. The pinnate leaves are in groups of 9 or 15, oval in shape and slightly sticky beneath. Spikes of pale blue, sweet-pea-like flowers appear from mid- to late summer, followed by small brownish-red seed pods.

Lobelia

Lobelia inflata

Campanulaceae

Indian tobacco, pukeweed

Lobelia has a similar action on the nervous system to nicotine and was smoked by Native American Indians to relieve asthma. Some herbalists still recommend the herb for bronchitis, but others consider it safe only for external use, as a soothing rub for bruising.

HABITAT Native to Canada and the eastern USA. Found in dry pastures, on roadsides, and in open woodland.

DESCRIPTION Annual with branched, hairy stems from 30–60cm(1–2ft) that contain a milky, acrid juice. The light green leaves are stalkless, oval and have serrated edges. Loose spikes of numerous tubular, blue, lipped flowers appear from mid-summer.

Lovage
Levisticum officinale

Umbelliferae
Love parsley

Lovage root has diuretic properties and was once employed in the treatment of jaundice and kidney stones. The root and seeds have digestive properties and may be made into a tea. Lovage was popular with Benedictine monks during the Middle Ages, for its medicinal, as well as its culinary properties. The leafy stems have a powerful, celery-like flavour and may be used in soups and potato salads. Try sprinkling the salty seeds on bread and cheese biscuits.

HABITAT Native to southern Europe and naturalized in North America, particularly the eastern USA. Cultivated in herb gardens.

DESCRIPTION Perennial with fleshy root and stout, grooved, hollow stems to 1.5m(5ft). The leaves are glossy, dark green and similar in appearance and smell to wild celery. From early to mid-summer umbels of tiny yellow flowers appear followed by brownish, grooved, aromatic fruit.

Lungwort
Pulmonaria officinalis

Boraginaceae
Jerusalem cowslip, spotted dog

To adherents of the Doctrine of Signatures, lungwort leaves resembled diseased lungs and were, accordingly, used to treat such pulmonary complaints as bronchitis. The herb has soothing and expectorant properties and is considered helpful for bronchial catarrh.

HABITAT Native to Europe and North America. Found on chalky soils in the shade of thickets and mixed woodland.

DESCRIPTION Perennial to 30cm(12ft) that is bristly all over. The stalkless leaves have characteristic white spots and are oval to egg-shaped with a slight point. The flowers are similar to cowslip and turn from pink to blue, appearing from early to late spring.

Mandrake

Mandragora officinarum

Solanaceae
Satan's apple

Mandrake is a poisonous, hallucinogenic plant that has been associated with magic since the time of the early Egyptians. The fruits were found in Tutankhamun's tomb and the root was a favourite ingredient of witches' brews. The plant also had a reputation as a love potion and in the Old Testament it was employed as a fertility charm. In Anglo-Saxon herbals, mandrake was reputed to exorcise demons from those who had become possessed. The most famous legend surrounding the plant, however, concerns the perils of uprooting it. When lifted from the earth, the mandrake would utter a piercing shriek that meant certain death, so an unfortunate dog was commonly entrusted with the task of pulling it. During the reign of Henry VIII, mandrake's human-shaped roots were thought to bring prosperity and changed hands for large sums.

The pain-killing properties of mandrake root were employed by the ancient Greeks, and in the Middle Ages mandrake wine was used as an anaesthetic during surgery. The root is a soporific and was formerly used as a sedative to ease rheumatic pains, convulsions and nervous disorders. In high doses, however, mandrake is a drastic purgative and can cause delirium. Today, mandrake is no longer used medicinally.

CAUTION Avoid. This plant is poisonous.

HABITAT Native to south-eastern Europe, Israel and Jordan, and the Himalayas. Grows on poor, sparse, sandy soils.

DESCRIPTION Perennial on stout, parsnip-like root that divides into two and resembles a pair of legs. The large, oval, fetid-smelling leaves grow to 30cm(12in), lie on the ground and have wavy margins. The five-petalled flowers appear on separate stalks and are whitish-yellow and tinged with purple. They are followed by round orange fruits that resemble a small apple.

Marigold

Calendula officinalis

Compositae

Mary bud

Marigold takes its botanical name from *calends*, Latin for the first day of every month, to emphasize its long flowering period. It is one of our most useful herbs and was used medicinally by the ancient Greeks, and probably by earlier Arabian and Indo-European peoples. In old English marigold was known as Golds, but later became associated first with the Virgin Mary, and later with Queen Mary. Looking upon marigolds was supposed to strengthen the eyesight, and the flowers were employed in the treatment of a wide range of ailments from headaches to red eyes and fevers. According to Culpeper, marigold strengthened the heart. The flowers followed the sun, and so came under Leo, the astrological sign ruled by the sun and associated with the heart. Modern herbalists, and also homeopaths, consider marigold a valuable wound-healing herb, and the ointment makes an excellent first-aid remedy for cuts, inflammations, bruises and burns. A compress is also helpful for varicose veins and an infusion of the flowers is a soothing eyewash for sore, irritated eyes. Internally, marigold is a useful digestive and can also help to bring on delayed menstruation.

Marigolds were commonly added to soups and stews in sixteenth-century Europe. They were planted alongside spinach and the two types of leaves were often combined and eaten like spinach. The yellow petals were made into puddings and were once used to colour cheese. Marigolds may, in fact, be used instead of saffron to colour rice, and they add a slightly peppery taste to the dish. The flowers make an attractive garnish for summer salads. The versatile marigold also has useful cosmetic properties. A strong infusion of the petals makes a healing and toning skin lotion for blemished skins, or a softening hair rinse that brings out red highlights in brown or reddish-brown hair.

HABITAT Native to southern Europe and parts of Asia. Introduced and distributed throughout northern temperate zones as a garden ornamental.

DESCRIPTION Familiar garden plant with a branching stem covered in fine hairs to 45cm(18in). The oblong leaves are hairy on both sides, with almost smooth edges and are pale green. The lower leaves are short stalked, the upper leaves clasp the stem. In late spring, daisy-like flowers with a double row of orange-yellow petals appear, and close up at night. The fruits are curved and ripen from green to brown.

GROWING TIPS Sow seed in a sunny position in spring, then thin out seedlings. Marigolds grow well in ordinary well-drained garden soil and need little attention.

Marjoram, Sweet

Origanum marjorana

Labiatae

Knotted marjoram

The generic name of the various species of marjoram, *Origanum*, is from the Greek *oros ganos* meaning 'joy of the mountain', a reference to the cheerful appearance and delicious smell of the flowering plant on Greek hillsides. The plant's common name, knotted marjoram, describes the curious, knotted shape of the flower buds. Marjoram has been cultivated for centuries as a medicinal and a culinary herb, and was introduced into Europe during the Middle Ages. In ancient Greece, marjoram had the reputation of bringing joy and comfort to both the living and the dead. It was customary to crown newly wed couples with marjoram, and if the herb grew on a tomb, the souls of the dead would find peace and happiness. According to an English custom, if a young girl annointed herself before bed with a mixture of dried marjoram, marigold, thyme and wormwood on St Luke's Day, she would dream of her future husband.

Medicinally, marjoram has similar properties to wild marjoram but is considered less effective. It was once used externally for sprains and bruises, and the dried, powdered leaves were taken as a snuff. Marjoram's principal use is culinary, and its warm, spicy flavour both complements and aids the digestion of meat. In Germany, marjoram's popularity is clearly reflected in its common name *wurstkraut*, or sausage herb, and it is widely used in stuffings and meat loaf. One of the most important herbs in European cuisines, fresh marjoram has a subtle aroma that is easily lost after lengthy cooking. Preserve it by adding the fresh leaf at the very end of cooking, and use it to flavour such lightly cooked dishes as scrambled eggs with mushrooms. Dried marjoram has a more robust flavour than fresh and is traditionally rubbed on to joints of meat before roasting.

HABITAT Native to North Africa and south-western Asia. Introduced and naturalized in the Mediterranean and Central Europe. Cultivated in North America and north-western Europe.

DESCRIPTION Spicy and aromatic perennial, usually grown as an annual, with square, branching stems from 30–60cm(12–24in). Sometimes grows to the size of a small shrub. The rounded leaves are opposite, greyish in colour and downy. From late summer to mid-autumn spherical, close heads of tiny white or pink flowers appear followed by tiny nutlets.

GROWING TIPS Sow seeds indoors or in a cold frame in early spring. Germination may be slow. Plant out in late spring in rich, well-drained soil, in a warm, sunny and very sheltered spot. Protect from frost and water sparingly.

Marjoram, Wild or Oregano

Origanum vulgare

Labiatae

Wild marjoram, or oregano, is often confused with its relative, sweet marjoram. Both plants are important culinary herbs but for medicinal use, wild marjoram is preferred. The chemical constituents of the plant include antiseptic thymol, and the herb also has anti-inflammatory, expectorant and digestive properties. Wild marjoram was gathered by the ancient Greeks for poultices and applied to sores, aching muscles, and joints swollen by rheumatism. According to Gerard, wild marjoram, like the sweet variety, would bring joy to the depressed and 'easeth such as are given to overmuch sighing'. Culpeper considered the plant a herb ruled by the planet Mercury and under Aries, and prescribed it as a tonic for the brain and head. After early settlers introduced the herb to North America, wild marjoram tea soon became a traditional remedy for such respiratory problems as bronchitis and asthma. The digestive properties of the herb made it useful for gastro-intestinal upsets, and a mixture of olive oil and wild marjoram was rubbed on rheumatic joints and sprains. Today, herbalists recommend wild marjoram for coughs, colds and flu, and as an antiseptic mouthwash for mouth and throat infections. A tea is also helpful for tension headaches, and the diluted oil eases muscular pains.

In culinary terms, wild marjoram is more usually referred to as oregano. It is used dried and gives pizza and spaghetti sauces their characteristic flavour. Italian oregano is a peppery, pungent-tasting herb, but the further north it is cultivated, the milder the flavour. In Mediterranean cookery, oregano gives a fine, strong flavour to bean casseroles, stews, and sauces based on tomato or aubergines.

Wild marjoram and other members of the *Origanum* genus were popular strewing herbs during the Middle Ages. The dried stems were sewn into sachets and used to scent washing water.

HABITAT Native to Europe and found from Iran westwards to Central Asia. Found on dry, stony soils on hillsides, banks and roadsides to 2000m(6500ft). Collected commercially in Italy and introduced and naturalized in the north-eastern USA. Found on chalk downs or limestone in the UK. Widely cultivated.

DESCRIPTION Aromatic perinnial, frequently bushy, with erect, hairy and woody stems to 60cm(2ft). The opposite greyish leaves are in pairs, with each pair at right angles to the next. They are broadly oval, pointed at the tip, and the upper leaves often have a reddish tint. From late summer to mid-autumn two-lipped, pinkish-purple or white flowers bloom in short terminal spikes.

GROWING TIPS In cooler climates the true flavour of wild majoram does not develop. For culinary use, plant sweet marjoram.

Marshmallow

Althaea officinalis

Malvaceae

Sweet weed

Althaea, marshmallow's botanical name, is from the Greek word for cure. All parts of the plant, especially the root, are rich in mucilage that soothes and heals soreness and inflammation. Early Arab physicians used marshmallow poultices to heal inflammations, and the ancient Greeks employed it for wounds, ulcers, and stings. Pliny, the Roman naturalist, held plants of the mallow family in high esteem and wrote 'Whosoever shall take a spoonful of the mallows shall that day be free from all diseases that may come to him'. For centuries, herbalists have prescribed decoctions or syrups of marshmallow for coughs, bronchitis and sore throats. Renaissance practitioners even employed marshmallow for gonorrhea. Today the soothing and healing qualities of the root are employed by herbalists to treat stomach ulcers, and for inflammations of the urinary tract. Externally the fresh leaves or a warm poultice made from the grated root are helpful for ulceration of the legs.

Marshmallow root has a sweetish taste but it is not an ingredient of, nor does it bear any resemblance to the sugary confectionery that is toasted over camp fires. Marshmallow was commonly eaten as a vegetable and the roots, first boiled and then fried in butter, were considered a delicacy by the ancient Romans. The emperor Charlemagne introduced cultivation of the plant into Europe, and in France the young tops of marshmallow were traditionally eaten in salads as a kidney tonic. Sweetish cough and throat lozenges, confectioners' pastes and syrups were once made from the gelatinous root, which may explain the origin of the name of today's popular confection.

HABITAT Native to Europe and naturalized in the eastern USA. Commonly found in moist places near the sea such as estuaries and salt marshes; also found in damp meadows and marshy wasteland.

DESCRIPTION Erect perennial from 1–1.2m(3–4ft) with a stout, tapering taproot that is yellowish on the outside. The stem and leaves are covered with soft hairs, and the greyish-green leaves are similar to those of the hollyhock – rounded to triangular, pointed and irregularly serrated. From mid-summer to early autumn five-petalled, pale pink or white flowers bloom in the leaf axils, followed by round, flattish fruits known as 'cheeses'.

GROWING TIPS Sow the seeds in a sunny but damp patch of garden, or in moist soil in a sunny position. Plant out at intervals of 60cm(2ft) and protect the seedlings from frost during the winter.

Meadowsweet

Filipendula ulmaria or *Spirea ulmaria*

Rosaceae

Queen of the meadow, meadwort

Sweet-scented meadowsweet is commonly known as queen of the meadow due to its tall, graceful appearance when in bloom and its habit of colonizing damp meadows. The flowers have a sweet, warm, almond-like scent, while the leaves are sharper and more aromatic. In fourteenth-century England the plant was known as meadwort since the leaves were used to flavour the sweet honeyed drink known as mead, and also added to wine and port. The leaves have a hay-like scent when dried and are still used to flavour summer wine cups as an alternative to woodruff. Meadowsweet was a popular domestic strewing herb that sweetened the indoor air during the summer months.

The scent of meadowsweet, according to Gerard, 'makes the heart merrie and joyful and delighteth the senses'. He prescribed the flowers for the ague, a fever with alternating burning and shivering, and for eye infections. The fever-reducing properties of the plant were scientifically vindicated in 1839 when an Italian professor found salicylic acid in the flower buds. This substance, also found in willow bark, was synthesized in 1889 and given the name aspirin – a word derived from meadowsweet's botanical name, *Spirea*. Salicylic acid, like aspirin, has anti-inflammatory properties and can also lower the temperature. Herbalists recommend meadowsweet for rheumatic and arthritic pain, and for feverish colds and flu. It is also considered one of the most effective remedies for heartburn and acid stomach and, unlike aspirin, it does not irritate the lining of the stomach or cause bleeding. Meadowsweet is a gentle remedy and its astringency is helpful for attacks of diarrhoea in children. Meadowsweet is also a useful cosmetic: meadowsweet flower water may be used as an astringent to tone the skin after cleansing.

HABITAT Native to Europe and Asia and introduced and naturalized in North America. Grows on moist, rich soils on the banks of streams and rivers, and in marshes and damp meadows.

DESCRIPTION Familiar perennial from 30–60cm(2–4ft) with stiff, reddish stems. The alternate, aromatic, feather-like leaves are toothed with two to five pairs of leaflets. They are dark green above and greyish-white beneath. Dense plumes of sweet-smelling, cream-coloured flowers bloom from mid-summer to early autumn, followed by spiral-shaped fruit.

GROWING TIPS Grow from seed sown in spring or autumn, or propagate by dividing the roots in spring. Meadowsweet prefers damp, rich soil with some shade and will flourish near water. Do not allow to get too dry in warm weather.

MINTS

Peppermint

Mentha piperita

Labiatae

In Greek myth *Mentha*, the name of the mint genus, was a lovely nymph pursued by Pluto, god of the underworld. Jealous Persephone found out about her husband's infidelity and turned Minthe into a low-growing plant that would be trodden underfoot. Fortunately, the plant also gave off a lovely aromatic scent. Culpeper, who knew the story, assigned the rulership of mint to Venus, planet of sexual attraction, and wrote that the herb 'stirs up venery, or bodily lust'. Peppermint was known to the early Egyptians and the Romans adorned themselves and their tables with mint.

Peppermint, curiously named since its taste is not peppery, was not employed medicinally until the mid-eighteenth century. It is the mint most widely used by herbalists on account of its menthol content. This valuable aromatic compound has cooling, anti-spasmodic, anaesthetic and decongestant properties. Peppermint tea has long been a popular domestic remedy for indigestion and its anti-spasmodic effect helps to relieve stomach aches and menstrual cramps. The tea acts as a general pick-me-up and can alleviate tension headaches and tiredness. Peppermint also stimulates gastric secretions, which promotes digestion, hence the tradition of after-dinner mints. Peppermint oil is a familiar ingredient of many brands of toothpaste, and combines an antiseptic action with a refreshing flavour. Menthol, with its cooling and anaesthetic action, is also found in rubs or massage lotions for aching muscles and rheumatic joints. Applying the fresh leaves is also said to ease muscular aches and pains. Menthol, too, makes an effective inhalation for clearing up catarrh and nasal congestion. Aromatherapists recommend a footbath of diluted peppermint oil for tired feet. Commercially, peppermint is widely used as a flavouring in the confectionery industry.

HABITAT Native to Europe and Asia. Widely distributed and naturalized in North America. Found in hedgerows, on the banks of streams, and on waste ground near dwellings. Rarely occurs in the wild in the UK.

DESCRIPTION A hybrid between spearmint (*Mentha spicata*) and water mint (*Mentha aquatica*). Familiar perennial with erect, square and slightly hairy stem from 60–90cm(2–3ft). The oval, very aromatic, toothed leaves have pointed tips and are smooth and dark green to reddish-green in colour. From late summer to mid-autumn elongated conical spikes of pinkish to mauve flowers grow at the tops of the stems.

GROWING TIPS Peppermint is a hybrid so cannot be grown from seed. Propagate by dividing the roots or root runners in spring and put into water to root. Plant out cuttings in moist, rich soil in a sheltered and partially shaded position. Mint is invasive so cut back regularly.

Spearmint

Mentha spicata

Labiatae
Garden mint

In sixteenth-century England, this herb was known as spere mynte and both this common name and *spicata*, the specific botanical name, reflect the spear-like shape of its leaves and flower spikes. This well-known culinary herb was introduced and promoted by the Romans who were very partial to its flavour. The naturalist Pliny declared that 'the smell of Mint doth stir up the minde and the taste to a greedy desire of meate'. Spearmint is a traditional English herb and has been grown in kitchen gardens since the ninth century. This herb was probably introduced into North America by the Pilgrim Fathers, and soon became established. In English cookery, mint sauce is the classic accompaniment to roast lamb, and the chopped fresh herb is particularly good with new potatoes, peas and young carrots. Spearmint has a milder flavour than peppermint and enhances fruit salads and fruit jellies, while its cooling properties have made it popular in summer drinks. In the southern USA, mint julep – a concoction based on fresh spearmint leaves, Kentucky bourbon, and crushed ice – became a fashionable cocktail during the nineteeth century.

Medicinally, spearmint has similar properties to peppermint but its effects are weaker. For this reason, and because of its milder taste, spearmint was considered more appropriate for children's ailments. Sweetened spearmint tea was used to treat upset stomachs, hiccups and vomiting in children.

During the Middle Ages, the stronger-smelling water mint *Mentha acquatica*, was a popular strewing herb. Mint leaves were also used to scent washing water and, according to seventeenth-century apothecary John Parkinson, 'used in Baths with Balm and other herbs as a help to comfort and strengthen the nerves and sinews'. Gerard noted that mint was 'applied with salt to the bitings of mad dogs', and also to wasp and bee stings. Culpeper recommended an antiseptic lotion of spearmint, plus a water-mint vinegar, as a wash for children with sore scalps and 'scurf'.

HABITAT Native to southern Europe and western Asia. Widely distributed. May be found wild as an escape in moist, fairly shady positions near habitation. Cultivated extensively as a culinary herb.

DESCRIPTION Perennial with straight, square stems to 60cm(2ft) and short-stalked, sharply pointed bright green leaves that are narrower and more lance-shaped than those of peppermint. The leaf edges are finely toothed and the undersides prominently ribbed. From early autumn narrow, tapering spikes of pinkish flowers grow at the top of the stem.

GROWING TIPS As for peppermint.

Mistletoe

Viscum album

Loranthaceae

Birdlime, European mistletoe

The name mistletoe is said to be derived from an Anglo-Saxon word, *misteltan*, signifying either 'bird-lime twig' because the berries were used to make birdlime, or 'different twig' because its branches are unlike those of its host tree. In pre-Christian times, mistletoe was understandably endowed with magical properties because of its mysterious growing habits – the plant was not propagated from seed but simply appeared high up in the branches of trees, and grew without soil. For the Druids, who worshipped the oak and used it medicinally, mistletoe berries symbolized the seed of the oak god. The plant was important in both medicine and fertility rites, as it drew on the oak's magical powers, and it was thought to offer protection from evil. At the winter solstice, the mistletoe was ritually cut down with a golden crescent-moon sickle by a white-robed Druid priest. This ceremony signified the death of the old year and the rebirth of the light with the new year. In the Christmas tradition of kissing under the mistletoe, traces of the ancient Druid fertility rites survive. In Norse mythology, mistletoe symbolizes death, since it is with a mistletoe spear that the blind god Hod kills the reputedly invulnerable Balder, god of light and son of Odin.

Mistletoe berries are poisonous to humans but not to birds, especially the appropriately-named mistle thrush. The leafy branches, however, were employed by seventeenth-century herbalists to treat epilepsy and nervous convulsions, and today the plant's active ingredients have been shown to act as a sedative, and to lower blood pressure by opening constricted arteries. Research is currently being pursued into the anti-tumour activity shown by mistletoe, and in Austria and Germany mistletoe extract is already being marketed in medications for delaying tumour growth.

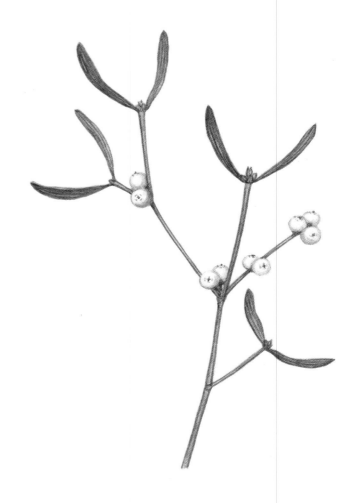

HABITAT Native to north-western Europe, extending south to the Mediterranean and eastwards as far as China. American mistletoe, *Phoradendron serotinum*, grows in the western states for New Jersey southwards as far as Texas; it has also been found in Missouri, Ohio and New Mexico. Grows on a wide range of deciduous trees, especially the apple. American mistletoe is said to prefer juniper trees.

DESCRIPTION Well-known evergreen parasite that takes root on the branches of deciduous trees, especially those with soft bark. A bushy, spherical, shrub with woody, yellowish-green stems to 1m(3ft) that fork into many branches. The narrow, bluntly oval leaves are a dull yellow-green and leathery in texture. From mid-spring to early summer small, inconspicuous flowers appear in the leaf axils and are followed by the familiar sticky, pearl-like berries that ripen in December.

Motherwort
Leonorus cardiaca

Labiatae
Lion's tail

Motherwort is a traditional sedative for treating the stress following childbirth. *Cardiaca* refers to the herb's tonic effect on the heart and circulation, and herbalists recommend motherwort for palpitations, and also for menstrual problems associated with tension.

HABITAT Native to Europe and introduced into northern USA. Found on banks, in hedgerows, along pathways, and on waste ground. Prefers well-drained, chalky soils. Rare in the UK.

DESCRIPTION Pungent-smelling perennial on stout, erect stem from 1–1.5m(3–5ft), that may be purple tinted. The downy leaves occur in opposite pairs up the stem and are divided into three to five deeply incised lobes. From mid-summer to mid-autumn whorls of bristly, pinkish-white flowers appear in the leaf axils.

Mountain Grape
Mahonia aquifolium

Berberidaceae
Oregon grape

The mountain grape is the emblem of the state of Oregon. Native Americans ate the berries and employed the bitter root to treat kidney ailments and skin diseases. Modern herbalists recommend mountain grape for chronic skin problems.

HABITAT Native to British Columbia and extending southwards through the mountainous north-west of America, from Oregon westward to Idaho and Colorado. Grows under coniferous trees on mountain slopes. Introduced and naturalized in Europe, and widely cultivated as an ornamental shrub.

DESCRIPTION Evergreen shrub from 1–2m(3–6ft) on brownish, knotty root with dense foliage. The leathery, dark green leaves are holly-like with prickly edges, and turn golden in autumn. The flowers are tiny, bright yellow and strongly scented. They are followed by dark bluish-purple berries.

Mugwort

Artemisia vulgaris

Compositae

St John's herb, Moxa

The English name of the plant is said to refer to its old use as a flavouring for home-brewed ale before the introduction of hops. According to another source, mug may be a corruption of an old English word *moughte* meaning a moth, since the plant, like wormwood, is a moth repellant. In the Middle Ages, mugwort was connected with John the Baptist, who was said to have worn a belt made of the herb during his time in the wilderness. St John's herb, as the plant became known, had the power to drive out demons, and sprays of the herb were worn around the head on St John's Eve as a protection against possession by evil forces. In China bunches of mugwort were hung in the home during the Dragon Festival to keep away evil spirits.

Mugwort contains a similar bitter principle to wormwood and has a tonic effect on the digestive system. Mugwort is also a mild sedative, and both Culpeper and Parkinson recommended the herb for hysteria. Its main use, however, is to regulate an erratic menstrual flow and to bring on delayed periods. In childbirth, a compress was traditionally employed to facilitate the expulsion of the afterbirth. Externally, dried mugwort may be added to the bath for aching muscles, and in both European and Chinese herbal medicine the herb is employed to relieve rheumatism and gout. Moxa is used in acupuncture, in the form of cones made from the downy leaf fibres. These are burnt very near to the skin to stimulate acupuncture points – a technique known as moxibustion.

HABITAT Native to Asia and Europe. Introduced and naturalized in North America as far south as Georgia and west to Michigan. Common on waste ground, on roadsides, and in hedgerows and ditches.

DESCRIPTION Erect perennial to 1m(3ft) with downy and grooved stems that are tinged with purple. The upper leaves have a faintly sage-like scent and resemble wormwood except that leaf segments have pointed, not blunted tips. They are pinnate and deeply incised, dark green above and a downy grey beneath. At the base of the stem, a rosette of leaves remains throughout the winter. From late summer to mid-autumn, long spikes of brownish-yellow to reddish flowers with five stamens appear at the ends of the stems. They are followed by tiny stick-like seeds.

GROWING TIPS Sow seeds indoors to help germination, then plant out seedlings in ordinary to poor garden soil in a sunny position. Mugwort may also be propagated by root division in spring or autumn.

Mullein, Great

Verbascum thapsus

Scrophulariaceae

Torches, donkey's ears, hag's taper

The plant's English name is from the Latin *mollis*, meaning soft, and reflects the velvety texture of its leaves. Donkey's ears is another reference to the woolly ear-like leaves. According to Parkinson, the tall dried stems were dipped in tallow to make tapers, hence the name torches. Mullein was also known as candlewick plant since, before the introduction of cotton or as a cheaper alternative to cotton, the dried down on the leaves and stem was used to make wicks for candles. The country name, hag's taper, means hedge taper and may have referred to the bright, candle-like appearance in a hedge of the tall spike of bright yellow flowers. Hag also means witch, and since witches were said to shelter in hedges, they too must have profited from the light provided by mullein wicks. In Homer's *Odyssey*, Ulysses took mullein to protect him from the temptations of the enchantress Circe, and in Europe and India the plant was reputed to drive out evil spirits.

Mullein leaves are rich in mucilage and were traditionally smoked to ease chest complaints. The flowering plant also has anti-spasmodic and expectorant properties, which explains its importance in the treatment of asthma, and particularly consumption – a once prevalent tubercular lung disease characterized by painful coughing spasms. Herbalists still consider mullein effective for a wide range of respiratory ailments, including bronchitis, asthma and catarrh. The flowers have sedative and soothing properties and a tea is thought to be helpful for insomnia. Macerating the blossoms in warm olive oil produces a pain-relieving lotion that has long been used as drops for ear-ache. The flowers yield a yellow dye, reputedly a popular hair colouring among the ladies of ancient Rome.

HABITAT Native to Europe and temperate Asia. Naturalized in the USA along the Atlantic coast, and common throughout the eastern states as far west as South Dakota. Grows on roadsides, in hedgerows, on waste ground, and grassy banks. Prefers chalky or gravelly soils.

DESCRIPTION Rigid, erect biennial that grows from a basal rosette of large, woolly leaves up to 2m(6ft) in the second year. The stout, stems bear large, thick, foxglove-like leaves and both stem and leaves are covered on both sides with a soft, grey felt. The leaves clasp the stem and have wavy margins. From mid-summer to early autumn, long, dense spikes of cup-shaped, lemon-yellow flowers appear with five rounded petals.

GROWING TIPS Sow seed in spring in well-drained, preferably stony stoil. Mullein is easy to grow and prefers a sunny position.

Mustard, Black

Brassica nigra

Cruciferae

The name mustard is derived from the Latin *mustum ardens*, meaning burning or fiery must, after the French practice of mixing ground mustard seed with must – fermenting grape juice. According to other sources, however, the English name is derived from the old French *moult ardre* or much burning. Black mustard is coarser and more pungent tasting than the white or brown varieties. It is mentioned in the Bible and was enjoyed by the ancient Greeks and Romans – they simply ground it on to their food and ate the young leaves in salads. In French Burgundy, fresh mustard sauce was especially popular and gallons were consumed with meat at feasts. Today, the name of the French city of Dijon is synonymous with fine mustards – a tradition that dates back to 1634. In medieval England, mustard was ground with honey and olive oil to make a runny sauce that was poured over meat. Centuries later, mustard was produced commercially in East Anglia, and in the city of Norwich British mustard manufacture continues to thrive. Most types of mustard were based on hand-harvested black mustard seed, until about the end of World War II, but with the increase of mechanized farming methods a more suitable plant, the milder brown mustard *Brassica juncea* was substituted.

Mustard has been used medicinally since the days of the ancient Greeks, principally for its warming and stimulating properties, although the seeds were once taken as a laxative. In America, the Mohegan Indians treated headaches and toothache with black mustard, while early settlers used mustard ointment to ease the pain of rheumatic joints. Mustard makes an excellent poultice for easing aching joints, and may be applied to the chest to relieve stubborn coughs. A hot mustard footbath is an age-old and effective domestic remedy for colds and poor circulation.

CAUTION Mustard may result in blistering in those with sensitive skin.

HABITAT Native to Europe, Asia Minor, China, India, North Africa, North and South America. Widespread throughout the world and found in hedges, on waste ground, roadsides, and sometimes on sea cliffs. Limited commercial cultivation.

DESCRIPTION Erect annual to 2m(6ft) with bluish-green to grass-green leaves and much branched stems. The leaves are alternate and the lower leaves are stalked, lobed and coarsely toothed. The shape varies from spear-shaped to oval or elliptic. The smaller upper leaves are entire. From summer to early autumn small, aromatic, bright yellow flowers are borne on twig-like stems. They have four rounded petals in the shape of a cross. These are followed by smooth, beaked seed pods that contain reddish-brown seeds.

Mustard, White

Brassica alba or *Sinapis alba*

Cruciferae

Yellow mustard

White or yellow mustard is closely related to Charlock or Wild Mustard (*Sinapis arvensis*), a common weed in cornfields. Like black mustard, it has long been employed as a condiment and a medicine but it is much less pungent. In the USA, white mustard forms the basis of yellow hot-dog mustard, and it is commonly added to brown mustard (*Brassica juncea*) in American mixed mustards. White mustard may be used in some English mustards but it is not an ingredient of Dijon mustard which is based on black and brown mustard seed. White mustard is particularly valued for its excellent preservative properties. It is commonly used whole as a pickling spice both for its flavour and to extend the keeping qualities of the pickle or relish. Young mustard seedlings, grown to the cotyledon stage, are also eaten in salads. They are the mustard in the familiar boxes of mustard and cress, although today rape seedlings are usually substituted.

Mustard seed, when crushed and mixed with water, forms a volatile oil that is responsible for its pungent smell and hot taste, and also acts as an appetite stimulant. This reaction, however, takes time to develop so when preparing dry mustard, leave it to stand for fifteen minutes before using. Purists advise against mixing mustard with vinegar, and suggest adding only prepared mustard, and not powdered, to such dressings as mayonnaise.

White mustard has similar medicinal applications to black mustard and the two may be mixed. White mustard may also be taken as a tea or added to the bath for feverish colds and influenza.

HABITAT Native to the Mediterranean region and western Asia. Introduced elsewhere. Originally an escape, now found wild in the UK and North America. Cultivated commercially.

DESCRIPTION Annual to 1m(3ft) with bright green, slightly hairy stems and alternate, pinnate leaves. The largest leaves are usually divided into three lobes with coarsely and irregularly toothed margins. From mid-summer to early autumn small lemon-yellow flowers appear like those of black mustard and with a similar smell. These are followed by horizontal, bristly seed pods that are ribbed, swollen and beaked at the tip. They contain yellow seeds. Black mustard seed pods are erect and smooth.

GROWING TIPS Sow seed in spring in a sunny position in rich, well-drained soil. White mustard is said to tolerate heavier soils than the black variety. Thin seedlings to 20cm(8in) and add compost regularly. Mustard self-seeds so harvest before the seed pods split open.

Myrrh

Commiphora molmol or *Commiphora myrrha*

Burseraceae

Gum myrrh

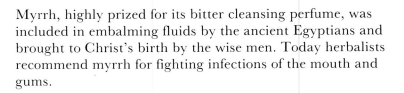

Myrrh, highly prized for its bitter cleansing perfume, was included in embalming fluids by the ancient Egyptians and brought to Christ's birth by the wise men. Today herbalists recommend myrrh for fighting infections of the mouth and gums.

HABITAT Native to the Middle East and East Africa. Grows in hot, arid regions on balsatic soils.

DESCRIPTION Hardy bush or small tree to 3m(10ft) with a stunted greyish-white trunk and knotted branches. The smaller branches terminate in sharp spines and bear a few oval, blunt leaves with coarsely toothed edges. The aromatic, pale yellow, gum resin seeps out naturally from fissures in the trunk, turning reddish brown and semi-transparent on hardening.

Nasturtium

Tropaeolum majus

Tropaeolaceae

Garden nasturtium, Indian cress

The Spanish conquistadors brought the Peruvian nasturtium to Europe, and it became a popular culinary and garden plant. The peppery-tasting flowers and young leaves add interest to salads, while the pickled flower buds may be eaten like capers.

HABITAT Native to South America, especially Peru. Widely cultivated as a garden ornamental.

DESCRIPTION Climbing perennial to 2.75m(9ft). Grown as an annual in cooler climates. The twining stems bear pale green, almost round leaves that are veined and have long stalks. From early summer to late autumn, trumpet-shaped flowers with spurs appear, ranging from orange-yellow to deep orange-red in colour.

GROWING TIPS Sow seed in early spring in a sunny location, in a light, well-drained soil. Nasturtiums also make good pot plants and will flourish on a sunny windowsill.

Nettle

Urtica dioica and *Urtica urens*

Urticaceae

Stinging nettle

The English name of the plant is thought to derive from an old Anglo-Saxon or Dutch word *noedl* meaning needle – either on account of its sharp sting, or because of the fibre in the plant. Nettle fibre has been used to weave cloth for centuries – a Danish Bronze Age grave contained nettle fabric and during World War I when cotton became scarce, both Austria and Germany made use of nettles. The fibre from the dried and soaked plant is similar to hemp, and it served a variety of purposes in the home from coarse sheets and cloth to sacking and fishig nets. The Scottish poet Campbell remarked, 'I have eaten nettles, I have slept in nettle sheets, and I have dined off a nettle tablecloth'.

The nettle has a long history of medicinal use. One remedy for arthritic pain consists of thrashing the painful area with the fresh stems, which act as a counter-irritant. Roman soldiers stationed in Britain reputedly chafed their skin with nettles to restore the circulation to limbs numbed by cold. The juice of the nettle is, surprisingly, an antidote to the pain of the sting, and dock leaves also dispel the irritation. Nettles do, however, lose their sting when boiled or dried. Nettles have a high iron and vitamin C content, which makes them useful in cases of anaemia. The fresh young tops were eaten as a spring tonic to cleanse the system after the stodgy food of winter. They may be added to salads or made into a soup. Many households brewed their own nettle beer to ease rheumatic pain, and nettle tea is still considered helpful for arthiritis and gout. Nettles are a traditional remedy for falling hair: the silica they contain strengthens the hair, giving fullness and shine.

HABITAT Native to temperate regions of Europe and Asia. Widely distributed throughout the world and naturalized in North America from Newfoundland westward to Colorado and southwards to South Carolina. Grows abundantly on waste ground, hedgerows, ditches, against walls and fences, and in gardens.

DESCRIPTION Familiar perennial from 90–180cm(3–6ft) with a single bristly stem, sparsely branched. The dull, dark green leaves are similar to those of mint. They are opposite, heart-shaped and taper to a point. The surface is covered with bristly, stinging hairs and the margins are finely toothed. From mid-summer to mid-autumn clusters of greenish, catkin-like flowers appear. The creeping roots spread quickly resulting in clusters of stems. *Urtica urens*, the lesser nettle, grows to only 1m(3ft). It is less downy than *Urtica dioica*, with smaller leaves and flowers.

Nutmeg and Mace

Myristica fragrans

Myristaceae

The origins of the culinary and medicinal use of nutmeg and mace are uncertain, but they were known to both the Indians and the Arabs during the sixth century. Nutmeg found its way into Europe by the twelfth century, and was one of the aromatic herbs and spices strewn in the streets of Rome to fumigate and deodorize them for Emperor Henry VI's coronation in 1191. By the beginning of the fourteenth century, the Arabs had identified the Indonesian Molucca islands as the principal source of nutmegs. The spice, however, did not become widely available until the Portuguese, having first opened a direct sea route to the East, reached and captured the Spice Islands at the beginning of the sixteenth century.

Nutmeg is an important culinary spice and a traditional flavouring for egg and cheese dishes, spinach, cakes and puddings, and such spiced meat mixtures as sausage and haggis. Mace, usually bought whole as a 'blade', has a stronger flavour and is particularly good with fish dishes, potatoes, and in chutneys.

Nutmeg, like many of the common kitchen spices, has digestive properties and can alleviate nausea and flatulence. In small doses nutmeg is mildly soporific, which explains its traditional use in milky nightcaps, such as eggnogs. In moderate to large doses, however, nutmeg is hallucinogenic, due to the active ingredient myristicin. This alkaloid has a similar structure to that of mescalin, found in the Mexican peyote cactus, and its effects – hallucination, double vision, rapid heartbeat, and disorientation – are also similar.

CAUTION Use nutmeg sparingly. Large doses may be fatal.

HABITAT Native to certain of the Indonesian islands, particularly the Moluccas, Malaya and the Phillipines. Introduced and cultivated in other parts of the tropics including the West Indies. Grows in shady locations in areas with a high degree of humidity, and on volcanic soils. May be grown as a hothouse plant in rich soil, providing humidity is high.

DESCRIPTION Tall evergreen tree to 9m(30ft) that appears bushy and flowers after around nine years. The bark is greyish brown in colour and smooth in texture. The

spreading branches bear aromatic, glossy, dark green leaves that are elliptical in shape and taper to a point. Umbels of yellowish male and female flowers appear in the leaf axils of separate trees and are followed by hanging, yellow or red plum-like fruit. On ripening and drying, the fruit splits open to reveal a brilliant red membrane or aril, known in its dried form as mace. The aril in turn encases the seed kernel known as the nutmeg.

Oak

Quercus robur

Fagaceae

English oak, tanners bark

The massive oak is a symbol of strength and durability, and it has along been one of northern Europe's most important construction timbers. Vast quantities were also used for constructing naval fleets, which severely depleted the extensive oak forests of England. During the naval assault on England by the Spanish Armada, a plot to burn down the great English oak forests and wreck the shipbuilding industry was, fortunately, unsuccessful. The oak is a symbol in Norse, Greek and Roman, and Celtic mythologies of the dwelling place of the principal male god, and signifies both strength and fertility. For the Vikings, the oak was designated Thor's favoured tree and as such it offered protection from lightning during thunderstorms. In Roman times, the oak was held sacred to Jupiter, king of the gods, and a crown of oak leaves, awarded to a man who had saved the life of a fellow soldier, was considered the highest military decoration. In Celtic Britain the oak was initially worshipped by the Druids. Later, when Christianity became the established religion, gospels were commonly preached beneath its shade and the tree was chosen to mark parish boundaries. An area in North London still bears the name Gospel Oak.

A tree of the gods was naturally invested with healing powers, and all parts of the tree were once employed medicinally. In medieval folklore, touching an afflicted part of the body with a nail, and then driving the nail into an oak was considered a cure for illness. The leaves were once applied to cuts, but today the bark alone is retained in herbal pharmacopeias. Oak bark's powerful astringency makes it an effective treatment for acute diarrhoea, while its antiseptic action is useful for treating throat infections. The bark was once drunk as a tonic tea, while a mixture of bark and acorns acquired a reputation as a poison antidote. The edible acorns were commonly roasted and ground to make coffee, and later fed to pigs.

HABITAT Native to the UK and northern Europe. Introduced elsewhere. Grows on moist, heavy clay soils but will tolerate sandy soils. Found in mixed woodland and lowland regions. The white oak *Quercus alba* is a North American native that is also used medicinally.

DESCRIPTION Familiar, robust deciduous tree to 40m(130ft) with a rounded, spreading crown and smooth, greyish bark that develops fissures with age. The oblong leaves have three to seven lobes on each side and with them appear catkin-like flowers. In autumn the fertile female flowers produce large numbers of the familiar greenish-brown acorns sitting in their cups.

Oats

Avena sativa

Graminaeae

Groats

Oats have a strengthening and tonic effect on a debilitated nervous system, and are helpful for nervous exhaustion and tension. Applied externally, an oatmeal poultice will soothe allergic skin conditions. Porridge and oatmeal biscuits, both rich in the B group vitamins, are traditional Scottish fare.

HABITAT Origin uncertain. *Avena sativa* is cultivated all over the world, particularly in Russia, North America and Scotland. It may be found wild as an escape.

DESCRIPTION Annual, tufted grass from 60–120cm(2–4ft) with a smooth, hollow, jointed stalk. The broad, flat, pale green leaves are rough in texture and taper to a point, and flowers are borne in small spikes at the end of the stems. After the flowers, swaying seed heads appear that contain the edible grooved grain.

Olive

Olea europeae

Oleaceae

The olive has been cultivated for over 3000 years and its Latin name is the origin of the word oil. Medicinally, olive oil has a mild laxative action and is reputed to lower blood cholesterol levels. Externally, warm olive oil is used to relieve earache, massage aching muscles, and condition dry, damaged hair.

HABITAT Native to the Mediterranean region, except Egypt. Introduced elsewhere and widely cultivated in warm to subtropical climates.

DESCRIPTION Small evergreen tree to 8m(25ft) with a slim trunk covered in greyish bark. The branches, often gnarled, bear opposite, lance-shaped leaves that are grey-green above and silvery beneath. Creamy, fragrant flowers appear in spring, followed by the familiar hard green oval fruit that ripens to dark purple.

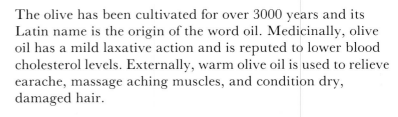

Orange

Citrus aurantium or *Citrus amara*

Rutaceae

Seville orange, bitter orange, bigarade

The English name of this tree is derived from the Arabic word *naranj* but the date of its introduction by the Arabs into Europe is uncertain. The Seville orange, as its name suggests, grows particularly well in Spain and its Moorish origin is clear from the similarity between *naranja*, the Spanish word for orange, and the Arabic *naranj*. It was this orange that was first grown in Europe, probably between the tenth and twelfth centuries. The sweet orange arrived later, with the return to Portugal of the explorer Vasco da Gama.

Seville oranges are grown principally for their heavily scented flowers, which are prized in perfumery. Essential oil of neroli is obtained from the flowers by distillation while the young leaves yield another essential oil, *petit grain*. Neroli is the basis of many perfumes and toilet waters, including eau de cologne, and is considered soothing and sedative by aromatherapists who use it to treat nervous anxiety and depression. Once the oil has been separated, the liquid residue is used to prepare orange flower water. This gives a delicate orange flavouring to biscuits and sweet dishes, and is traditionally used in Middle Eastern cookery. In cosmetic terms, this flower water makes an excellent skin tonic that is good for dry, sensitive skins. Orange blossom is a traditional English wedding flower.

Seville oranges provide the refreshing tartness characteristic of good marmalade, and their rind gives the best flavour when cooking. In classic French cookery, such savoury dishes as duck *à l'orange* are improved by using Seville orange rind instead of the sweet variety. Bitter orange peel is considered helpful for the digestion, especially for dyspepsia and flatulence. It forms the basis of many, predominantly French, liqueurs including Cointreau, Grand Marnier, and Curaçao. Dried orange peel makes a good addition to spicy pot pourri mixtures, and pomanders made out of whole oranges studded with cloves keep clothes smelling fresh and moth-free.

CAUTION Oranges may aggravate arthritis.

HABITAT Native to Arabia and possibly southern China. Introduced and naturalized in Europe, particularly southern Spain, Florida, and California. Also cultivated in the Caribbean.

DESCRIPTION Evergreen tree to 8m(25ft) with smooth, greyish-brown bark and spiny branches. The glossy, dark green leaves are paler beneath and oval in shape. Very fragrant creamy white flowers with thick, fleshy petals bloom in the axils and are followed by the familiar globular fruit, flattened at the top and the base. The seville orange has coarser and darker skin, and a more bitter-tasting pulp than the sweet orange.

Pansy, Wild

Viola tricolor

Violaceae

Heartsease

Pansy, derived from the French *pensée*, was a popular ingredient of love potions and was reputed to alleviate painful emotional separations. In Shakespeare's *A Midsummer Night's Dream*, the juice of this flower inspires Titania's passion for Bottom. Medicinally, the wild pansy is a traditional remedy for such skin diseases as acne, eczema, and psoriasis.

HABITAT Native to Europe and naturalized in North America. Grows in hedgerows, on cultivated grassland, and wood edges.

DESCRIPTION Annual or perennial to 15cm(6in) with a soft, hollow stem and spoon-shaped, opposite leaves with rounded lobes, not heart-shaped like those of the violet. The pansy-like flowers vary in colour and are usually a mixture of bright purple, white and yellow. The lower petal is spurred at the base.

Parsley Piert

Aphanes arvensis

Rosaceae

Breakstone

Parsley piert, due to its habit of breaking through and rooting in stony ground, was pronounced a cure for urinary stones and gravel by adherents of the Doctrine of Signatures. The herb is a powerful diuretic that is soothing to the urinary tract, and herbalists still recommend it for painful urination and for dissolving urinary gravel.

HABITAT Native to the UK and common in Europe in fields, on stony waste ground, and on the top of stone walls.

DESCRIPTION Low-growing annual with a short, slender stem and small, wedge-shaped green leaves that are deeply cut into three to five lobes. The whole plant is downy and bears tufts of tiny, inconspicuous greenish flowers from spring to late summer.

Parsley

Petroselinum crispum

Umbelliferae

Curly-leaved parsley

Both the botanical and English names of this herb are derived from the old Latin *Petros selinon*, or Rock Celery. To the ancient Greeks, curly-leaved parsley was honoured as a plant of death, and it was customary to strew the leaves over corpses and to make them into wreaths for decorating tombs. At this time, parsley had an exclusively ceremonial use. Later, it appeared on the table at Roman banquets, both for its flavour and also for its breath-freshening properties. In European folklore, parsley's notoriously slow germination period gave rise to the superstition that its roots went down to the devil seven times before the plant would grow. The herb also acquired a reputation as a poison antidote, possibly due to its powerful deodorizing effect.

Herbalists consider parsley a kidney and liver tonic, as well as a digestive, and a tea is helpful for bladder problems, rheumatism and flatulence. Scientific analysis has shown parsley to be a highly nutritious herb. It is a rich source of vitamin C, containing more by volume than an orange, and also contains iron, calcium and vitamins A and B. Health-giving parsley is the most widely employed of all European culinary and garnishing herbs. It brings out the full flavour of food, especially fish sauces, and combines well with other herbs, as in the classic *fine herbes* and *bouquet garni*. Chewing fresh parsley will rid the breath of garlic or onion odours.

HABITAT Native to the Mediterranean, and possibly eastwards to the Lebanon. Introduced and naturalized elsewhere, particularly in the UK, northern and central Europe. Widely cultivated as a garden herb and commercially. Prefers rich, moist soils. May be found wild in rocky places as an escape. Mediterranean or flat-leaved parsley, the other common variety of parsley, is more popular on the Continent. It is a hardier plant and better adapted than the curly-leaved variety to extremes of temperature.

DESCRIPTION Familiar biennial to 60cm(2ft) on a stout taproot with branching stems. The bright green leaves are deeply segmented and tightly curled over. In the second year, umbels of tiny greenish-yellow flowers appear in early summer, followed by small, ribbed fruits (seeds). The flat-leaved variety has more feathery, celery-like leaves that lie flat and are a darker shade of green.

GROWING TIPS Sow seeds in early summer in a rich, moist soil where there is a little shade. Encourge germination by pre-soaking the seed in warm water, and water well in hot weather.

Pasque Flower

Anemone pulsatilla

Ranunculaceae
Wind flower

Pasque flower is a species of anemone, a name derived from the Greek *anemos*, meaning wind. Both the common name of windflower and the plant's specific botanical name *pulsatilla*, meaning pulsing or beating, refer to the waving motion of the plant's frail stems when a breeze is blowing. Gerard, the celebrated sixteenth-century English herbalist, christened the plant pasque flower because it blooms over the Easter period. He recommended the plant for eye infections characterized by watering and discharges, and, interestingly, the plant has long been associated with weeping. In Greek myth, the pasque flower sprouted from ground that was wet with Aphrodite's tears, while homeopaths prescribe the plant for sensitive people who are easily moved to tears.

Herbalists consider pasque flower, with its mild sedative action and muscle relaxant properties, a valuable remedy for menstrual cramps, especially when they are accompanied by tension or anxiety, and also for nervous headaches. Pasque flower may also be prescribed for ovarian pain and inflammation of the reproductive organs. This delicate plant also has antibacterial properties that are helpful for such skin infections as boils, and it combines well with Echinacea. In homeopathy, the pasque flower is referred to by its botanical name *pulsatilla*, and is a valuable remedy for treating children. It is particularly suited to weepy, clingy children, and may be prescribed for ailments characterized by discharges, such as colds and catarrh.

CAUTION The fresh plant is poisonous and should only be taken as directed by a qualified practitioner. The infinitesimal dosages used in homeopathy do not present the same risks.

HABITAT Native to Europe and introduced elsewhere. Found wild on dry, grassy slopes and chalk downs throughout northern and central Europe. Prefers well-drained, light chalk and limestone soils, and open sunny situations. Grown horticulturally as a garden ornamental.

DESCRIPTION Perennial from 10–25cm(4–10in) on a thick rootstock that sends up bunches or a rosette of finely divided leaves, and slender flowering stem. Leaves, stems and flowers are all covered with soft, silky hairs, and most of the leaves develop after the flowers have appeared. The lovely six-petalled single flowers appear from late spring to mid-summer and are a matt dark purple with yellow stamens. They are followed by attractive, fluffy seed heads with small, brown, hairy-tailed seed vessels.

GROWING TIPS Sow seeds in spring in a light, well-drained, preferably chalky soil, choosing a sunny position, Other varieties are available horticulturally and are very attractive garden plants.

Passionflower

Passiflora incarnata

Passifloraceae

To seventeenth-century Spanish settlers in South America, the passionflower appeared as a divine symbol of Christ's crucifixion. In its elaborate, finely cut and ringed corona the Spanish Jesuit priests saw the crown of thorns. The coiling tendrils and pointed leaves symbolized the whips and spears of Christ's persecutors, while the five anthers represented the five wounds. Early settlers interpreted the appearance of the passionflower as a God-given sign of approval for their task of converting the indigenous South American people to Christianity. Passionflower still has a symbolic function: it is the state flower of Tennessee.

Passionflower is a valuable sedative that calms the nerves and has antispasmodic properties. Native South Americans applied the leaves to bruises, and made a soothing tea from the woody vine. In the latter half of the nineteenth century, passionflower extract became an official preparation in the USA and was prescribed for insomnia, hysteria, seizures and nervous exhaustion. The plant was commonly included in herbal sedatives and was also smoked for its mild narcotic effect. Some considered the flower an aphrodisiac. Today, herbalists value passionflower for its non-addictive tranquillizing properties and recommend it for recurrent insomnia, anxiety and tension. In small doses, the dried herb has no known toxicity and may be made into a relaxing tea. Added to the bathwater, passionflower also has a soothing effect. The edible fruit, known as granadilla, is sweet and juicy. It is an ingredient of some juice mixtures and refreshing summer drinks.

HABITAT Native to northern regions of South America, and the southern USA, from Florida westwards to Texas and north-westwards to Ohio. Found wild in thickets, along fences and wood edges where there is some shade. Cultivated elsewhere in temperate zones.

DESCRIPTION Perennial, hairy vine that climbs by means of coiling tendrils and grows from 3–9m(10–30ft). The woody stems bear alternate, lanceolate leaves that are divided into three finely toothed lobes. From early to late summer beautiful, sweet-scented flowers appear with five white to pale lavender petals and a striking purple, ringed corona. These are succeeded by an edible, yellow to orange berry that is oval and contains many seeds.

GROWING TIPS May be grown from seed or from cuttings in deep, fertile, well-drained soil. Water well and provide some shade from strong sunlight. In cooler climates passionflower may need the warmth of a greenhouse with partial shade in summer. Replace the topsoil with a newly fertilized layer each spring for best results. The fruits of ornamental varieties of passionflower are not always edible.

Peach

Prunus persica

Rosaceae

The origin of the peach tree is uncertain but it is thought to
have come from China. The tree is mentioned in the writings
of the Chinese philosopher Confucius in the fifth century BC,
and is also represented on antique Chinese porcelain and
other artefacts. As its specific botanical name suggests, the
tree was introduced to Europe from Persia, probably by the
Romans. By the first half of the sixteenth century, the peach
had appeared in England and was cultivated in the
celebrated London garden of Gerard.

According to the old herbals, peach leaves were capable of
expelling worms from the body. To this end, either a poultice
of the fresh leaves was applied externally, or an infusion of
the dried leaf was drunk. In Italy, peach leaves were
considered a cure for warts. After applying the fresh leaf to
the wart, it was buried in the ground and left to decay, by
which time the wart should have disappeared. Culpeper
maintained that the dried and powdered leaves would stop
bleeding and hasten the healing of sores and wounds. In
modern herbalism, the leaves are not used extensively but
may still be recommended for an irritated digestive tract.
Both bark and leaves have been traditionally employed in
whooping cough and bronchitis.

As early as the seventeenth century, Culpeper recognized
the cosmetic importance of peach kernel oil. He pounded the
kernels with vinegar and boiled them to a thick paste,
declaring that the mixture 'marvellously causes the hair to
grow again upon any bald place or where it is thin'. Today,
peach kernel oil is still an ingredient in many hair-care
products, and is used for massage, and as a moisturizer.

HABITAT Familiar fruit tree that is widely cultivated all over
the world in warm and temperate climates. In the southern
USA, California is best known for its peaches.

DESCRIPTION Medium-sized tree that resembles the plum
and can reach 8m(25ft), although trees in orchards are
usually pruned to keep them shorter. The fast-growing and
spreading branches bear oblong leaves that taper to a sharp
point and have serrated edges. They hang in groups of two or
more on slender shoots. Before the leaves are fully open,
dainty, pale pink five-petalled blossoms appear that have
very little odour. The familiar fruit with its even texture and
delicate bloom is similar in structure to the plum and
apricot. The sweet-tasting pulp surrounds a hard stone with
an oil-filled kernel inside.

Pennyroyal

Mentha pulegium

Labiatae

European pennyroyal, run-by-the-ground, pudding grass

Pennyroyal's specific botanical name is from the Latin *pulex*, meaning flea. In Roman times, the herb was a popular flea repellant and the leaves were either burnt in infested rooms or scattered over bedding. Rubbing fresh pennyroyal leaves on the skin will deter insects, and the herb is also reported to keep pets free from fleas. Sprinkle the dried herb on pets' bedding, or use a pennyroyal infusion as a flea shampoo.

Pennyroyal has long been employed to bring on delayed menstruation. According to Culpeper, writing in the seventeenth century: 'The herb, boiled and drunk, provokes women's courses and expels the dead child and the afterbirth'. The oil extracted from the plant is a powerful abortifacient of long standing, but large doses are required and these have proved fatal. A number of women with unwanted pregnancies have died after using the oil, and relatively small quantities have resulted in irreversible kidney damage, convulsions and coma. Pennyroyal leaves are less hazardous but some herbalists suggest peppermint as an alternative. Native Americans drank pennyroyal tea for cramping pains and to relieve colds. In England, too, a hot tea made from the leaves was a traditional home remedy for colds and chills. Pennyroyal provokes sweating, hence its effectiveness as a cold cure. American pennyroyal has the same properties and uses.

In culinary terms, pennyroyal was once used to flavour savoury black puddings and for stuffings. Today, its pungent taste is considered overpowering and disagreeable.

CAUTION Pennyroyal causes the muscles of the uterus to contract and should be avoided during pregnancy.

HABITAT Native to Europe and western Asia. Found on rich, moist and sandy soils, often in ditches, near streams and pools. American pennyroyal, *Hedeoma pulegiodes*, found in fields and open woods, is common in the eastern USA.

DESCRIPTION Aromatic perennial belonging to the mint family, growing either low along the ground or erect to 30cm(12in). The square, branching stems bear oval, slightly hairy, greyish-green leaves with serrated or scalloped edges. They give off a pungent, mint-like smell. In late summer, two-lipped lilac-blue flowers bloom from the leaf axils, forming dense whorls up the stem. American pennyroyal is a more upright plant that grows to 40cm(16in) and has longer leaves than the European variety.

GROWING TIPS European pennyroyal is easily propagated from cuttings or by dividing the roots and planting them in rich, moist soil with some shade in summer. American pennyroyal is usually grown from seed and prefers a dry soil and a sunny position.

Pepper

Piper nigrum

Piperaceae

Black pepper

Of all the spices, pepper has long been held in the highest esteem. The Romans were importing pepper in the fifth century, and the search for the source of this lucrative spice led to the discovery of a sea route to the East. Pepper became such a valuable commodity that during the siege of Rome in AD 408, Attila demanded part of the city's ransom in pepper. During the Middle Ages, it was comparable with gold and silver and the fortunes of the great Italian city of Venice were directly attributable to its trade in pepper. As late as the fifteenth century, rents in England were commonly paid in pepper, as it was considered more stable than the currency of the time. Paradoxically, the term 'peppercorn rent', has now come to mean a nominal or trivial amount.

Unripe pepper berries are picked and then dried until they become the familiar dark brown to black, wrinkled peppercorns. The flavour of freshly ground black pepper is superior to that of ready ground, and in cooking it has become practically indispensable. White pepper is from the same plant as black but is produced using a different method. The berries are left on the vine to ripen and then the hard outer skin is removed by soaking. Most white pepper, however, is black pepper with the skin stripped off by machine.

Pepper's principal use is as a seasoning and condiment, but it also has digestive properties. It contains an alkaloid that stimulates the taste buds, and this in turn causes saliva and gastric juices to flow. Pepper has been employed medicinally for indigestion and flatulence, and also externally to encourage circulation. Aromatherapists also value the warming qualities of essential oil of black pepper. They recommend it for colds and digestive problems, and use it diluted to massage painful muscles.

HABITAT Native to South India and the East Indies. Found in tropical forests and requires shade and high levels of humidity. Introduced and cultivated commercially in such tropical countries as India, Indonesia, Sri Lanka, Brazil and the West Indies. Often grown alongside other crops in plantations – for example, coffee.

DESCRIPTION Perennial climbing vine with strong, woody stems that can reach 6m(20ft) but are usually pruned to 3m(10ft). At the joints of the branched stems are broad, glossy, oval leaves that taper to a point. They are dark green in colour and prominently veined. Small white flowers are followed by hanging clusters of round, green or yellow berries that ripen to red.

Periwinkle

Vinca major

Apocynaceae
Greater periwinkle

Both the common and the botanical names of this plant are derived from the Latin verb *vincare*, meaning to bind or subdue, a reference to its invasive creeping stems. To the ancient Romans the periwinkle was a symbol of sacrifice and death, and in medieval England it was associated with executions. An old Italian tradition involved laying wreaths of periwinkle on the graves of dead babies, and the plant was known as *fiore di morte*, flower of death. Periwinkle has an old reputation as a magical herb and was popularly known as the Sorcerer's Violet. It was a common ingredient of love potions, including a ghastly concoction which necessitated mashing up the plant with earthworms and houseleek. Culpeper assigned the periwinkle to the planet Venus and writes that 'the leaves eaten together by man and wife cause love between them'. In France, the periwinkle is a symbol of friendship.

Medicinally, periwinkle is an astringent, healing herb. The fresh leaves were applied to wounds and inserted into the nostrils to stop nose bleeds. An ointment of the bruised leaves was considered very effective for piles. Periwinkle is still regarded as a valuable astringent and a tea may be recommended for over-profuse menstruation, and also for bleeding gums. Periwinkle also acts as a mild sedative, and has been taken for nervous anxiety. The Madagascar or Rosy Periwinkle *Catharanthus roseus*, a related species, is a traditional African folk remedy for diabetes. In 1950 researchers who were investigating the plant's reputed anti-diabetic properties discovered that it acted on the white blood cells to inhibit cancer growth.

HABITAT Native to Europe. Grows in woods, thickets and hedgerows on well-drained chalky and loamy soils. Familiar garden plant.

DESCRIPTION Perennial hedgerow plant with trailing or climbing stems from 30–90cm(1–3ft) that form a dense covering. The shiny, oval leaves are either blunt or sharp pointed, and are borne in pairs up the stem. They remain throughout the winter. From mid-spring to early summer attractive purple-blue flowers appear with five blunted, triangular petals that resemble the blades of a fan.

GROWING TIPS Propagate from cuttings or from seed and plant in ordinary garden soil in a shady position. The stems can be invasive and may be employed as ground cover. The Madagascar periwinkle may be grown in pots or outside as a bedding plant, but will not tolerate frost.

Peruvian Bark

Cinchona

Rubiaceae

Quinine tree, fever tree, Jesuits' bark

The common names of this tree give a clear indication of its medicinal value. Native South Americans first employed the bark for fevers and passed on their knowledge to the invading Spanish conquistadors and missionaries in the sixteenth century. As the common name suggests, Spanish Jesuit priests prescribed the powdered bark medicinally and it was finally introduced to Spain in the mid-seventeenth century. By 1677, the bark was officially listed in the London Pharmacopeia but the tree was not identified and listed botanically until 1737. The Latin name of the species is in honour of the Countess of Cinchon who actively promoted the medicinal qualities of the bark. The cinchona is the source of quinine, a valuable substance that was widely employed as an antimalarial agent in the tropics. Synthetic drugs have been introduced to treat malaria but the parasites, transmitted by mosquitoes, that cause the disease can become resistant to them. Quinine, however, is still used against malaria.

Peruvian bark is still prescribed by herbalists for feverish conditions in general, and it is valued as a digestive aid. The bark has a very bitter taste that stimulates the digestive juices and acts as a general tonic on the digestive system as a whole. Quinine water was once a popular beverage, usually mixed with spiritis such as gin. Peruvian bark has a calming effect on the heart and is useful for an irregular heartbeat. Quinidine, a drug originally derived from the cinchona tree, is employed in orthodox medicine for regulating the heartbeat.

CAUTION Peruvian bark stimulates contractions of the uterus so should be avoided during pregnancy. Excessive doses may cause blindness and deafness. Use only as directed by a qualified practitioner.

HABITAT The cinchona species are native to the Andes in tropical America, especially Peru and Ecuador. Also grown in India, East Africa, Burma, Sri Lanka and Java.

DESCRIPTION Evergreen tree from 6–25m(20–83ft) that grows in mountainous regions, becoming shrubby at very high altitudes. The variable leaves are usually elliptical to oval and pointed, and are bright green in colour. They are veined with prominent mid-ribs. The lilac-like flowers are very fragrant and deep rose-red, and in the species used medicinally, the corolla is ringed with hairs.

Pine, Scots

Pinus sylvestris

Pinaceae

Scots fir

The fresh-scented oil distilled from pine needles has powerful antiseptic properties. Both the oil and an infusion of the needles are employed medicinally as decongestants to alleviate sinusitis, bronchitis and catarrh. Pine cones produce the kernels used in Mediterranean cookery.

HABITAT Conifer that extends over a wide area from the Scottish and Spanish mountain ranges, eastwards to Siberia. Grows wild in mountainous areas, usually on light, sandy or rocky soils. Grown as an ornamental in parkland and widely cultivated in plantations.

DESCRIPTION Tall coniferous tree to 35m(114ft) with a straight, cylindrical, unbranched trunk and a conical crown. The bark is a distinctive rust colour and the flat, bluish-grey needles are always in pairs. From late spring to early summer orange flowers appear and the female variety turn into small green cones. These swell and take two years to ripen into woody, greyish oval cones.

Plantain

Plantago major

Plantaginaceae

Greater plantain, rat's tail

To the old Anglo-Saxon herbalists, plantain was a valuable remedy for poisonous bites. Externally, a poultice of the fresh leaves is a traditional remedy for wounds, sores and stings.

HABITAT Native to Europe; introduced and widespread in other temperate zones, including North America. Common on cultivated land, on roadsides and waste ground.

DESCRIPTION Common weed from 15–30cm(6–12in) with a basal rosette of blunted, oval, prominently veined leaves. Distinctive, erect, cylindrical flower spikes appear from late spring to early autumn. They are composed of tiny, purplish-green to yellowish-green flowers.

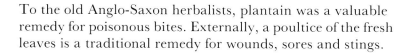

Pleurisy Root

Aesclepias tuberosa

Asclepiadaceae

Flux root, butterfly weed

Pleurisy root, as its name suggests, is specifically employed for lung problems and respiratory infections. The plant is a traditional Native American remedy, and was one of the ritual herbs of the Appalachian Indians.

HABITAT Native to North America along the east coast, in the Appalachian region, and as far west as Arizona. Common in dry fields and along roadsides, on sandy or gravelly soils.

DESCRIPTION Attractive perennial to 60cm(2ft) with thick, hairy stems growing from a stout knotty root. The alternate leaves are hairy, spear-shaped and deep green. From mid-summer to mid-autumn beautiful orange flowers appear in terminal umbels.

Poke Root

Phytolacca americana

Phytolaccaceae

Pokeweed, pigeon berry

Poke root is a traditional Delaware Indian remedy for rheumatism, but it is a drastic purgative in large doses. Early American settlers used the purple juice from the berries as a writing ink and a fabric dye.

CAUTION The whole fresh plant, including the berries, is poisonous.

HABITAT Native North American plant from New England south to Florida and Texas. Naturalized all over Europe. Found on the edges of fields, on cleared land and roadsides.

DESCRIPTION Bushy perennial on a thick, brown, branched root with green or purplish stems from 120–270cm(4–9ft). The oblong leaves taper to a point and give out an unpleasant smell. From late summer to mid-autumn, clusters of white or purplish flowers appear at the ends of the stems, followed by clusters of round green berries that ripen to deep purple and resemble blackberries.

Pomegranate

Punica granatum

Punicaceae

The common name of this juicy fruit is a corruption of *poma granata*, Latin for many seeded apple. The botanical name refers not only to its many seeds, but also to the source of the fruit in Roman times: Punicus or Carthage, a Roman colony in North Africa. The fruit was mentioned in the Egyptian Ebers Papyrus, written about 2000 BC, and is mentioned in the Old Testament. The striking red colour and seed arrangement of the pomegranate made it one of the earliest and most important symbols of fertility, and it is an ancient design motif. The pomegranate is reputedly the 'forbidden fruit' eaten by Eve in the Garden of Eden, and the fruits were said to be represented on the pillars of King Solomon's temple. In Greek mythology, Persephone or Kore was abducted by Pluto to his underworld kingdom. There she ate a pomegranate, a symbol of union, that forever bound her to Pluto.

The medicinal qualities of the pomegranate were known to Pliny in the first century. He recommended the root bark for expelling tapeworms, for which it is an effective but nauseating remedy. In traditional Indian medicine, the bitter rind is used to treat dysentery. Its powerful astringent properties are also helpful for diarrhoea. The leaves, too, have antibacterial properties and were once applied to sores.

In culinary terms, the pomegranate is most widely used in Middle Eastern cookery. The thickened juice is used to flavour meat dishes, especially stews, and the dried seeds are used as a garnish. In Indian cuisines, the seeds may be found in stuffings for savoury breads and pastries. The fruit has a refreshing taste and is made into drinks and desserts, while the juice is the basis of the liqueur grenadine.

HABITAT Native to Asia, particularly Iran, Afghanistan and the slopes of the Himalayas. Naturalized in warm, dry climates including the Mediterranean, Palestine, North Africa, and eastwards to India and Pakistan. Cultivated commercially, and dwarf forms may be grown horticulturally in temperate regions.

DESCRIPTION Small deciduous tree or bush to 6m(20ft) with pale brown bark and slender branches with spines at the tips. The leaf buds and young shoots are red, and the opposite leaves are oval in shape, thick and glossy. Large, waxy, orange-red flowers are followed by the familiar reddish-yellow skinned fruits. These are the size of an orange with a tough, outer rind and many seeded, pinkish-red pulp.

Poppy, White
Papaver somniferum

Papaveraceae
Opium poppy

Records concerning the use of the opium poppy date back 5000 years to the time of ancient Sumerian civilization. The medicinal qualities of the plant were well known to the Egyptians, Greeks and Romans, and the poppy was cultivated in China, India and Iran in the eighth century. The specific botanical name of the plant, *somniferum*, means sleep-inducing, while opium is a corruption of the Greek *opion*, meaning sap or juice. Opium, the valuable substance yielded only by this species of poppy, is a thick, milky latex that is extracted via incisions made in the unripe seed heads, just after the plant has flowered. It contains around 25 different alkaloids, notably morphine and codeine, the powerful pain killers that are extensively used in orthodox medicine.

Medicinally, the opium poppy is valuable for its pain-killing, sedative, antispasmodic and expectorant properties. In the eighth century an Arabian physician developed an opium-based cough syrup that remained popular until the seventeenth century. During the Middle Ages, a sponge impregnated with an infusion of poppy juice, mandrake, hemlock and ivy served as an early form of anesthetic. It was held under the patient's nostrils during surgery. Later, a tincture of opium known as laudanum became a popular sedative in Victorian times, and opium smoking inspired many artists and writers. Opium abuse continues today: the opium poppy is the source of heroin, a morphine derivative.

The ripe seeds of the opium poppy, surprisingly, contain no narcotic alkaloids, neither does the oil extracted from them. These tiny grey-blue poppy seeds give a nutty flavour to bread, biscuits, and cakes, and are also used in Indian curries, both for flavouring and as a thickening agent.

HABITAT Native to the Middle East, also western Asia and south-eastern Europe. Introduced and naturalized in other parts of Europe and may be found wild on waste ground as an escape. Widely cultivated in South-east Asia, principally as a source of opium.

DESCRIPTION Annual with rigid pale green stems, usually with a few bristles on the flowering stalks. The leaves are oval to heart-shaped with coarsely indented margins and are pale greyish- to bluish-green in colour. From mid- to late summer large, four-petalled delicate flowers appear that vary in colour from white or bluish-white, often with a purple blotch at the base of each petal, to pale lilac or deep pink. These are followed by oval green seed capsules, ringed at the base and with a flattened top surmounted by a disk. The tiny seeds are usually blue-grey in colour.

Prickly Ash

Zanthoxylum americanum

Rutaceae

Toothache tree

Native American Indians chewed prickly ash bark to alleviate toothache, and it is a traditional remedy for rheumatic pain. Both the bark, and especially the berries, stimulate the circulation and are helpful for such disorders as cramp and chilblains.

HABITAT Native to North America from Canada south to Nebraska and Virginia. Found in wooded areas on rich, moist soils.

DESCRIPTION Shrub or small tree to 3m(10ft) with sharp spines on the branchlets and leaf stalks. In early spring, small yellow-green flowers appear in the axils before the leaves. The oval, pinnate leaves are dark green in colour with a pleasant lemon scent. Inky blue berries, surrounded by a grey shell, grow in clusters on top of the branches.

Pumpkin

Cucurbita pepo

Cucurbitaceae

Pumpkin fragments found in Mexico that date back 4000 years testify to its value as a food crop. Pumpkin pie is a traditional American Thanksgiving dish, and pumpkin lanterns are hung up at Hallowe'en. Herbalists recommend the seeds for expelling worms, and their hormone-like action is helpful for prostate problems.

HABITAT Probably native to the eastern Mediterranean. Widely cultivated in warm and temperate climates, including the USA and the UK.

DESCRIPTION Trailing annual vine with long, branched stems to 6m(20ft) bearing large, rough, triangular lobed leabes similar to those of the squashes. From early to mid-summer, attractive funnel-shaped deep yellow flowers appear, and the flowering stalks swell and ripen into the familiar, bright orange, ribbed fruit that may weigh as much as 12kg(25lb).

Purslane

Portulaca oleracea

Portulacaceae

Garden or green purslane, pigweed

Fresh purslane has been eaten in India and the Middle East for centuries. The wild variety was introduced into Europe during the Middle Ages and several varieties were developed from it, notably green and golden purslane. In England, cultivation of garden purslane is thought to have begun relatively late, in the second half of the sixteenth century.

Purslane has a rather sharp taste, and may be eaten raw, boiled or pickled. In Middle Eastern cookery, the cooked plant is added to a traditional bread-based salad called *fattoush*. In France, it was customary to prepare the classic soup *bonne femme* with equal parts of sorrel and fresh purslane. Purslane was a popular salad herb in Elizabethan England and the fresh, young leaves were 'familiarly eaten alone with Oyl and Vinegar' (John Evelyn). For winter use, the thicker stems of older plant were salted and pickled in vinegar. At the end of the eighteenth century, purslane fell out of favour. Today it is rarely eaten in England, although some recipes suggest steaming the young stems in the manner of asparagus.

Gerard considered purslane a valuable cooling remedy and applied the fresh herb to the temples for fevers and pains in the head. Culpeper prescribed the herb for painful gout, and the leaves were commonly applied to sores and inflammations. Purslane also acquired a reputation for easing the pain of sensitive teeth – 'teeth that are set on edge with the eating of sharpe and soure things' (Gerard). Later, the fresh plant was found to be a rich source of vitamin C and so was employed in the prevention of scurvy. Purslane tea also has diuretic properties and was drunk as a tonic. Today the herb is rarely used medicinally.

HABITAT Developed from the wild variety that probably originated in the Middle East. Widespread in temperate and sub-tropical zones from China west to Europe. Naturalized in North and South America and also found in the UK. Prefers dry, nitrogen-rich soils and sunny situations.

DESCRIPTION Sprawling annual with fleshy stems from 15–30cm(62in) that are tinged with pink. The thick, succulent leaves grow in clusters and are bright green and spatulate. In late summer solitary or groups of two to three small yellow flowers appear, blooming for only a short period.

GROWING TIPS Sow seed in spring in light, well-drained soil. Plant out seedlings 15cm(6in) apart in a sheltered, sunny position and water well. The leaves are ready for harvesting after six to eight weeks. Golden purslane or *Portulaca sativa*, a sub-species, is not so hardy but has attractive yellow leaves.

Pyrethrum

Chrysanthemum cinerariifolium

Compositae

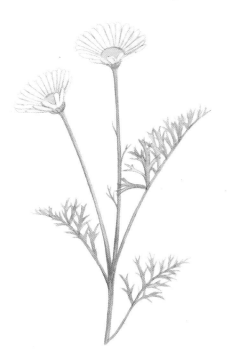

The insecticidal properties of a related species of pyrethrum flower were discovered by the Persians. Later, the Dalmatian pyrethrum was found to be more effective, and it has become one of the best-known, non-chemical pesticides for controlling aphids on both outdoor and indoor plants.

HABITAT Native to coastal areas of Yugoslavia and its islands. Prefers chalky or pebbly shores but is also found inland on dry, stony hillsides. Cultivated commercially in Japan, South Africa, and California.

DESCRIPTION Tall perennial from 30–75cm(12–30in) with slender, hairy stems, and dark green leaves deeply incised and divided into seven segments. From early summer to early autumn, solitary, white daisy-like flowers appear.

Quassia

Picrasma excelsa or *Quassia amara*

Simarubaceae

Bitter ash

The quassia tree was named in honour of a Guyanese slave who used it to treat fevers. The wood is intensely bitter and is employed medicinally to stimulate the appetite and aid digestion. Quassia wood has insecticidal properties. An infusion of the bark was once taken to expel intestinal worms. Today a garden spray made from the chips helps to eradicate aphids and red spider.

HABITAT Native to the West Indies; also found in tropical South America. Grows wild on plains and low mountain slopes.

DESCRIPTION Tree resembling the ash to 20m(65ft) with smooth, greyish bark. The pinnate leaves are oblong and pointed at both ends, and from late autumn inconspicuous yellowish-green (red in *Q. amara*) flowers appear. These are followed by shiny black berries the size of a pea.

Quince

Cydonia oblonga

Rosaceae

The quince has been in cultivation since the earliest times, and was well known to the ancient Greeks. The botanical name *Cydonia* refers to Cydon on the island of Crete, the source of the best variety of quince trees. The common name is derived from *quines*, the plural of the old French name for the fruit. Historically, quinces are thought to be the golden apples referred to in classical literature and Greek mythology, since oranges were unknown in Greece and Italy until the time of the Crusades. The quince was the sacred fruit of Aphrodite, or Venus, and statues often depict her holding a fruit in her right hand. This is a reference to the coveted 'golden apple' awarded to her by Paris in recognition of her beauty. As a symbol of the love goddess, a single quince was traditionally eaten by the bride and bridegroom at the marriage ceremony to promote harmony and happiness. This custom survived into the Middle Ages when quinces were presented as tokens of love, and eaten at wedding breakfasts 'to be a preparative of sweet and delightful days between the married persons' (*The Praise of Musicke*, medieval text).

Hotter climates are said to produce sweeter and juicier quinces than cooler countries, where quinces tend to be very tart and rather fibrous in texture. English quinces require boiling, sweetening, and sometimes straining, and are almost always turned into jelly and marmalade.

Medicinally, the quince was highly esteemed by the Roman historian Pliny, and was known in Shakespearean England as 'the stomach's comforter'. The fruit is astringent, and a syrup was once employed for diarrhoea but today, the seeds are the only part of the quince that is used by herbalists. These swell up in water and are employed for their gentle laxative properties, in the same manner as linseed or psyllium. Like the fruits, the seeds are also astringent and may be helpful for inflammations and soreness in the mouth.

The quince is related to the Japanese quince, japonica, or *Chaenomeles japonica*. It is a popular garden ornamental but rarely produces fruit in cooler climates.

HABITAT Native of Iran, Turkey and parts of Greece. Widely cultivated in the Near East, and introduced and cultivated in tropical America and warm climates, including the Mediterranean and southern Europe.

DESCRIPTION Small deciduous tree or shrub to 3m(9ft). It is much branched and similar in appearance to the pear and apple, with large, solitary white to pink flowers. The fruit is very fragrant, golden in colour, and round or pear-shaped.

Raspberry

Rubus idaeus

Rosaceae

European wild raspberry

It has been established from archeological excavations that wild raspberries have been picked and eaten since prehistoric times. Raspberries were first grown for their fruit during the Middle Ages, and all the cultivated varieties were developed from the wild species. Raspberries have long been a popular summer fruit and traditionally made into jams, jellies, vinegar, brandy, and such liqueurs as *framboise* from north-eastern France. Home-brewed raspberry vinegar fulfilled a dual function since it was administered for fevers and sore throats, as well as being used for cooking and drinking. Rasberries are rich in iron and vitamin C.

The leaf is the most valuable medicinal part of the raspberry, and the herb has a long history of use in preparing expectant mothers for childbirth. Raspberry-leaf tea is traditionally drunk during the last three months of pregnancy to strengthen the uterus and pelvic floor muscles, and ease the pain of contractions during labour. Raspberry leaf tea was also drunk by women to prevent miscarriage, and it can help to check blood loss during birth. The gentle astringency of raspberry leaves is also helpful for diarrhoea in children, and an infusion makes a good mouthwash for ulcers and bleeding gums.

Rubus strigosus, the North American wild red raspberry, is related to the European raspberry and is commonly found in thickets and heaths throughout North America. The leaves, like those of the European variety, have a long tradition of use in pregnancy and a tea is said to relieve nausea and vomiting.

HABITAT Native to Europe and Asia. Introduced elsewhere. Found in woodland clearings, wood edges, railway embankments and on heathland. Prefers moist, nutrient-rich soil and grows up to altitudes of 2000m(6500ft). Cultivated garden varieties have been bred from this wild species.

DESCRIPTION Shrub with perennial roots and biennial, woody stems to 1.5m(5ft) that usually have prickles but occasionally lack them entirely. The oval leaves have markedly serrated edges and are arranged in groups of three or seven. The underside is downy. From spring to summer in the second year, clusters of small, white flowers appear in the upper axils. They are followed by the familiar, fragrant, cone-shaped red berries that are reminiscent of blackberries but much softer.

GROWING TIPS Cultivated varieties are propagated from root cuttings and then planted out at intervals of 60cm(2ft) in rich, loamy soil with canes for support. Replace plants every three to four years.

Rosemary
Rosemarinus officinalis
Labiatae

Rosemary is a corruption of the Latin *ros marinus*, or dew of the sea, after the plant's habit of growing in coastal areas. In ancient Greece, rosemary's reputation for improving the mind and the memory led Greek students to wear garlands around their heads while sitting exams. Later, rosemary came to signify remembrance and at funerals the mourners carried fresh sprigs to toss into the grave – a sign that the deceased would not be forgotten. Rosemary featured at weddings as an emblem of fidelity, and sprays were traditionally included in the bride's bouquet. Anne of Cleves wore a rosemary wreath when she married Henry VIII. Tapping your lover with a fresh sprig of rosemary was said to ensure constancy.

Rosemary's connection with the head persists since herbalists recommend it for headaches. The oil is an old remedy for gout, and muscular aches and pains, and it was the active ingredient of the celebrated Hungary Water that restored life to Queen Elizabeth of Hungary's paralyzed limbs. During the fifteenth century, people burnt rosemary branches in their homes to protect themselves from the black death, and in World War II rosemary and juniper were burnt in French hospitals to limit the spread of infection. According to an old supersition, sleeping with a sprig of rosemary under the pillow would banish both evil spirits and nightmares.

In the home, rosemary is a popular kitchen herb. Its pungent flavour complements roast lamb, poultry and fish, as well as a variety of vegetables. In cosmetic terms, rosemary stimulates the head and scalp, and the oil is a popular ingredient of hair tonics and shampoos.

HABITAT Native to the Mediterranean and widely cultivated in temperate climates as a garden plant. Grows wild on rocky Mediterranean hillsides near the sea and prefers light, dry, chalky soils. Several early-flowering cultivated varieties are available.

DESCRIPTION Very aromatic evergreen shrub to 1.5m(5ft) with numerous branches that are downy when young and later become woody with greyish-brown, scaly bark. The narrow, leathery leaves are spiky, with a dark green upper surface and a pale grey, downy underside. When rubbed they give off a strong scent with camphor-like overtones and a hint of pine. From spring to early summer two-lipped, pale blue flowers grow in clusters towards the ends of the branches.

GROWING TIPS Propagate from cuttings taken in summer that have had time to develop roots. Plant out in a sheltered, sunny position in well-drained, chalky soil and protect from frost during the winter.

Rowan

Sorbus acuparia

Rosaceae
Mountain ash

The rowan is not a relative of the ash, but of the wild service tree. The common name is thought to be of Scandinavian derivation, from the Norwegian *raun* or the Swedish *ronn*. The tree has a long association with magic and there are many old superstitions surrounding the tree, usually concerning its protective power. In rural areas, it was customary on the eve of May Day to hang bunches of rowan twigs tied with red ribbons over barn doors so the livestock would be protected from evil spirits. In the same way, wearing a necklace of rowan berries would keep a farmer's wife safe from the influence of witches. A good crop of rowan berries in the autumn was held to signify a poor harvest the next year.

Rowan berries are astringent and rather acidic. The juice has been used medicinally as a gargle for sore throats and laryngitis, and its astringency was useful in treating haemorrhoids. The fruit contains vitamin C and was formerly employed in the prevention of scurvy. Sweetened with sugar, the strained jelly is a good substitute for cranberry sauce and may be served with game. A tart jelly may also be made from crab apples and rowan berries. In the north of England, the berries were added to meat dishes, while in northern Europe they were fermented to produce a strong spirit. Rowan-berry ale was once drunk in Wales.

HABITAT Native to northern Europe. Grows in deciduous forests, on moors, heaths and rocky slopes. May be found at altitudes of over 1000m (3250ft) and is common in areas with high precipitation. Planted in towns, parks, and gardens as an ornamental.

DESCRIPTION Deciduous tree to 10m (30ft) with smooth, shiny grey to greyish-brown bark. Although not related to the ash, the leaves are similar: they are oblong with serrated edges and grouped pinnately, usually with six to seven pairs. From spring to early summer, small creamy white flowers appear in flat-topped umbels, and are followed by green, pea-sized berries that quickly ripen into attractive, bright orange-red berries. In autumn, the leaves, too, turn a bright scarlet.

Rue

Ruta graveolens

Rutaceae
Herb of Grace

To the ancient Greeks, rue offered protection from ailments induced by witchcraft, such as indigestion after a meal with strangers. Later, medieval Europeans were still eating the herb to safeguard themselves from sorcery. Rue was also considered a powerful defence against poisoning by the celebrated first-century herbalist, King Mithridates, and its reputation as a poison antidote was still intact in Elizabethan times. According to Gerard, 'If a man be anointed with the juice of rue, the poison of wolf's bane, mushrooms, or toadstooles, the biting of serpents, stinging of scorpions, spiders, bees, hornets and wasps will not hurt him'. Later, sprigs of rue were placed in court to protect the judge from 'jail fever' – contagious diseases carried by the prisoner. Rue is the 'sour herb of grace' referred to in Shakespeare's Richard III, and in Catholic churches, bunches of the herb acted as sprinklers for holy water before High Mass. Rue came to symbolize the grace that follows repentance, and in wordplay, to rue means to repent or regret.

The ancient Romans considered rue beneficial for the eyes, and artists and crafts-people ate rue to sharpen their eyesight. Monks working on medieval manuscripts took rue to ease headaches brought on by eyestrain, and today herbalists still recommend small doses of the herb for strained eyes and associated headaches. Rue acts specifically on the uterus and may be employed to treat menstrual disorders. The herb was once used as an abortifacient and should not be taken during pregnancy. Externally, rue is thought to be helpful for rheumatic pains and homeopaths prescribe it for sprained wrists and ankles.

The Romans used rue in cooking, but today it is seldom used on account of its overpowering taste. It may still be added to certain varieties of the Italian spirit *grappa*.

HABITAT Native to southern Europe and North Africa. Grows in hilly regions on poor, dry, rocky ground in sheltered situations. Widely cultivated in temperate climates, including the UK and North America, where it is also found wild as an escape on roadsides and waste ground.

DESCRIPTION Hardy, shrubby perennial to 60cm(24in). The lower stems are woody and bear alternate bluish-green leaves that are deeply subdivided into small, spatulate leaflets. The leaves have a curious, pungent smell and a bitter taste. From summer to early autumn, yellowish-green flowers with four-toothed petals grow in loose clusters towards the ends of the stems.

GROWING TIPS Sow seed in late spring and transplant seedlings to a sheltered, sunny position. Rue prefers well-drained, chalky soil.

Saffron

Crocus sativus

Iridaceae

Saffron crocus

The saffron crocus has been cultivated since antiquity, and is represented in Cretan art dating back to 1600 BC. The dried stigmas yield an orange dye that has long been an important, and costly, item of trade, and is still an important culinary spice and colouring. In eastern Asia, kings and holy men wore robes dyed with saffron, and both colour and fragrance were highly prized by the ancient Greeks. The ancient Chinese imported it from Persia and the Arabs introduced it into Spain in the tenth century. The plant's common name is thought to be derived from the Arabic *zafaran*. Cultivation reached the rest of Europe by the twelfth century, and from the fourteenth to the early twentieth century, the Essex town of Saffron Walden was the centre of English saffron growing.

Saffron is a fragrant and expensive spice. The stigmas must be picked by hand and estimates of the number of flowers needed for just one pound of saffron vary from 35,000 to 200,000. Saffron was a popular kitchen spice in medieval England and was employed in both sweet and savoury dishes. Today, the high cost precludes extensive use and turmeric is often substituted, especially in Indian cookery. Gourmets consider saffron essential for classic Spanish *paella* and the French soup *bouillabasse*. Yellow Cornish saffron cakes are traditionally eaten in the South West of England.

As a medicine, saffron was well known to Culpeper who assigned it to the planetary rulership of the Sun, possibly due to its yellow colour, and recommended it for 'fainting fits and the palpitation of the heart'. Saffron also enjoyed a reputation as an aphrodisiac, but today it is no longer used medicinally. In medieval times, saffron was a popular hair dye.

HABITAT Native to Asia Minor but now unknown in the wild. Widely cultivated in temperate regions, particularly Spain and France, also India, and China. Formerly cultivated in the eastern UK. Grown horticulturally. Not to be confused with the wild and poisonous meadow saffron.

DESCRIPTION Typical crocus that is perennial and has no stem. In spring grass-like leaves rise directly from the corm and are greyish-green in colour with sheathed bases. From early autumn, fragrant mauve, purple or reddish-purple six-petalled flowers appear. They have three distinctive orange-red stigmas and long yellow anthers.

GROWING TIPS Plant corms in a rich, sandy soil in autumn at a depth of 10cm(4in) and at 15cm(6in) intervals. Choose a sheltered spot and protect from frost.

Sage

Salvia officinalis

Labiatae

Garden sage, narrow-leaved sage

The botanical name of the sage genus *Salvia* is from the Latin verb *salvere* meaning to save, and refers to its considerable medical reputation in ancient times. Sage was so highly esteemed that by the tenth century it had acquired the reputation of conferring immortality, an exaggerated claim that persisted well into the seventeenth century when John Evelyn wrote of sage: 'It is a plant indeed with so many and wonderful properties that the assiduous use of it is said to render men immortal'. Sage, too, was thought to reflect the business fortunes of the man of the house, flourishing or withering according to the state of his finances.

At one time, a flourishing trade in sage was carried on between China and Holland. The Chinese, having acquired a taste for sage tea, offered the Dutch large quantities of their own green tea in exchange for supplies of the herb. Sage tea was at one time as popular as Indian tea, but was principally drunk for its health-giving properties. The Chinese considered sage tea strengthening to the digestive system, and also valued its calming properties. Gerard recommended sage for 'shaky trembling of the members' and the herb is still employed for nervous excitability and nervous headaches. Sage is a traditional remedy of long standing for soothing sore throats, on account of its antiseptic and antibacterial properties. Culpeper recommended a hot sage infusion for an inflamed throat and hoarseness, and a gargle of sage mixed with a little vinegar and honey is particularly effective. In feverish conditions, sage is very cooling and herbalists also prescribe it for colds and for easing hot flushes during the menopause. Fresh sage leaves rubbed on the teeth will deodorize the mouth and strengthen the gums. This versatile herb has also been of cosmetic value since Roman times when a strong infusion of the herb was a popular hair darkener.

Sage, seldom used in cooking until the sixteenth century, is now one of the commonest kitchen herbs in European cookery. In English cooking, sage and onion stuffing is traditionally served with such fatty meats as pork, duck and goose, while in Italy sage is used as a flavouring for liver and in the classic veal dish *saltimbocca*. Sage goes well with cheese and is used to make one of England's popular regional cheeses, Sage Derby. The plant is also very attractive to bees and makes excellent honey. Sage, especially the dried herb, has a powerful flavour that can be overpowering unless it is used with discretion.

HABITAT Native to the northern Mediterranean coast, particularly Yugoslavia where it is found wild in the hills. Prefers poor, dry limestone soils in sunny situations. Over 750 species of sage are widely cultivated throughout the world in temperate zones, and as far north as Canada. Several varieties with variegated leaves are grown horticulturally.

DESCRIPTION Hardy, shrubby, branching perennial from 30–70cm(12–30in) that is strongly aromatic. The young stems are covered with a white down but become woody at the base as they age. The surface of the thick, velvety leaves is puckered and veined, and the underside is hairy. The leaves are greyish-green and oblong with rounded ends. From early to mid-summer whorls of tubular, two-lipped, violet-blue flowers appear at intervals towards the ends of the stems.

GROWING TIPS Sow seed in late spring or, for use the same year, propagate by layering or from cuttings. Sage prefers a well-drained soil and a sunny, sheltered position. Prune well in spring and renew woody plants every three to four years.

RED SAGE

Salvia officinalis purpurea

CLARY SAGE

Salvia sclarea

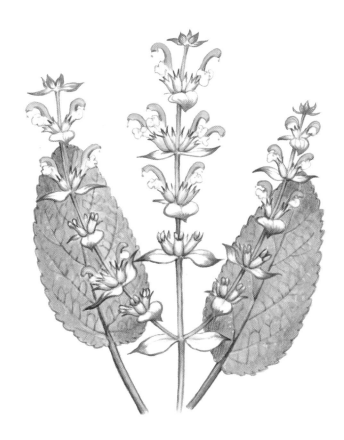

This is a variant of garden sage that has purple-red foliage and grows to 45cm(18in). It is propagated by cuttings or by layering since the seeds usually revert to the green-leaved type. It is thought to be even more effective for sore throats than garden sage and is also good for bleeding gums and mouth ulcers. It may be used in cooking in the same way as garden sage.

This grows to 1m(3ft) and has large, oblong leaves with toothed margins that are dull green in colour and wrinkled. The generic botanical name and the common name come from the Latin word *clarus* meaning clear, and the herb is also known as clear eye. When the seeds are soaked in water they become mucilaginous and the liquid was traditionally used to clear the eyes of grit and other foreign bodies. The leaves, together with elderflowers, were used to flavour German wines that then became more potent Muscatels, and the German name for the herb was *mustkateller*. Clary sage is cultivated commercially for its balsamic-scented oil that is used in perfumery. Arometharapists consider clary sage a warming, uplifting and soothing oil and employ it for stress, tension and muscular aches. It is a biennial that may be grown from seed and prefers dry, well-drained soil.

St John's Wort

Hypericum perforatum

Hypericaceae

Common St John's wort

The history of St John's wort has long been bound up with magic and mysticism and the plant was employed as a kind of herbal exorcist. In pre-Christian times sprays of the plant were suspended over icons to sanctify the atmosphere and drive away evil spirits. According to a superstition once prevalent on the English Isle of Wight, the consequence of stepping on St John's wort at dusk was a terrifying night spent on the back of a fairy horse. With the advent of Christianity, the herb became associated with John the Baptist. It was in full bloom on St John's day, and was reputed to bleed on the anniversary of the saint's beheading. When crushed, the red pigment in the flower petals stains them red, like blood.

This curious bleeding plant was considered effective for healing wounds by the early Greek herbalists, and it was used to dress sword cuts in the Middle Ages. Later, in the eyes of the English adherents of the Doctrine of Signatures, the leaf glands resembled holes, and so the plant was destined for 'hurts and wounds and inward bruises'. Modern analysis has revealed the plant's antibacterial and astringent properties, both of them useful in speeding up the healing of cuts and wounds. Macerating the flowers in oil yields a sedative, analgesic rub that alleviates neuralgia. Homeopaths use St John's wort to treat cuts, wounds, and post-operative pain.

HABITAT Native to Europe and western Asia. Naturalized in North America, especially along the East Coast, South America, Australia, and New Zealand. Grows in meadows, hedgerows, grassy banks and roadsides, on dry, gravelly soils. Grown as a garden ornamental and spreads rapidly. Shrubby varieties are popular for rockeries.

DESCRIPTION Spreading, aromatic, hardy perennial with long runners and an erect stem, branching at the top, that grows to 60cm(2ft). The round stem may be distinguished by two raised ridges running up its length. The pale green leaves are small and oblong and are dotted with translucent oil glands. From late summer to mid-autumn clusters of five-petalled yellow flowers appear at the ends of the stems and are marked with small black oil glands. The whole plant gives off an incense-like scent.

GROWING TIPS Propagate from seed, from cuttings, or by root division. St John's wort will flourish in ordinary garden soil and prefers a sunny position, but with some shade.

Sandalwood

Santalum album

Santalaceae

The musky oil extracted from the aromatic wood of this Indian tree has long been endowed with aphrodisiacal properties. Sandalwood oil has also been used medicinally for bronchitis and cystitis, and aromatherapists consider it an aid to relaxation.

HABITAT Tree native to India, particularly Mysore in southern India.

DESCRIPTION Small tree from 6–9m(20–30ft) with smooth greyish-brown bark and straight-grained white to yellow stem wood that dries to light reddish-brown and is very aromatic. The branches are slender and drooping and bear opposite, oval leaves that taper to a point and are often covered with a white bloom. The small, stalked flowers vary in colour and bloom in erect, pyramidical clusters at the ends of the branches.

Sarsaparilla

Smilax officinalis and spp.

Liliaceae

Honduras sarsaparilla, red sarsaparilla

In the sixteenth century sarsaparilla acquired a reputation as a potent cure for syphilis, for which it continued to be prescribed until the beginning of the twentieth century. Today, sarsaparilla is considered a blood-purifying herb that is beneficial for such skin diseases as psoriasis, and also for rheumatism. Jamaican sarsaparilla is made into a soft drink.

HABITAT Native to Central America and found in tropical Amazonian rain forests, in swamps and on river banks.

DESCRIPTION Climbing or trailing vine with arrow-shaped, veined leaves and woody stems that rise from a long, tuberous, knotted rootstock. The stems bear sharp prickles and climb by means of tendrils. The small, greenish to white flowers grow in umbels from the leaf axils.

Sassafras

Sassafras albidum

Lauraceae

Sassafras root, a well-known native American remedy for fevers, became an important medicinal export during the sixteenth century, and was even sold as a cure for syphilis. Sassafras oil is toxic but the root bark acts as an antiseptic and is considered safe for external application to cuts, sores, and poison ivy rash.

HABITAT Native to eastern North America from Michigan southwards to Florida and eastwards to Texas. Grows on wood edges and waysides on sandy soils.

DESCRIPTION Aromatic deciduous tree to around 9m(30ft) with rough, greyish, fissured bark. In spring, before the leaves have formed, clusters of pale yellow-green flowers appear. The alternate leaves are usually three lobed, with downy undersides. The fruits are pea-sized berries and dark blue in colour. Both the bark and the leaves have a refreshing fennel-like fragrance.

Saw Palmetto

Serenoa serulata

Palmae

Native Americans considered the ripe fruits of the saw palmetto a tonic and an aphrodisiac. The berries do, in fact, have a toning effect on the male reproductive system and have been employed for impotence and prostate problems.

HABITAT Native to North America along the Atlantic coast from Texas through Florida northwards to South Carolina. Grows in dense patches on swampy, low-lying coastal plains.

DESCRIPTION Low shrubby palm from 1–2m(3–6ft) with creeping underground stems that produce a crown of green palm-like leaves that are often coated with white and have sharp, saw-toothed stalks. Inconspicuous flowers appear in clusters, followed in autumn by berries that resemble black olives when ripe.

Self Heal

Prunella vulgaris

Labiatae

Heal-all, carpenters' herb, woundwort

Exponents of the Doctrine of Signatures prescribed self-heal for sore throats and mouth inflammation on account of the plant's tubular, throat-shaped flowers. Self-heal's wound-healing properties were valuable after domestic disputes, and the plant was also known as carpenters' herb.

HABITAT Native to Europe, North America and Asia and introduced elsewhere. Common in meadows, grassland, and open woodland, on moist soils in sunny situations.

DESCRIPTION Perennial on square, grooved stem to 20cm(8in) that may be erect or low growing. Pairs of opposite, hairy leaves are spaced regularly up the stem and are oblong to ovate. Compact spikes of lipped, violet flowers appear from mid-summer to early autumn at the tips of the stems with a pair of stalkless leaves beneath, like a collar.

Senna

Cassia senna

Leguminosae

Alexandrian senna

Senna, known to Arabian physicians as early as the ninth century, is an effective and long-established remedy for constipation. It is best combined with such digestives as ginger or cloves that will improve the taste and prevent griping pains.

HABITAT Native to North Africa, Egypt, the Sudan and Jordan. Indian senna, *Cassia angustifolia*, is native to southern India.

DESCRIPTION Perennial shrub to 60cm(2ft) with pale green, erect stems and spreading branches. The leaves are grouped in four to five pairs and are lance-shaped, brittle in texture, and greyish green in colour. Erect spikes of small, five-petalled yellow flowers are followed by oblong pods containing about six seeds.

Shepherd's Purse

Capsella bursa-pastoris

Cruciferae

Pepper and salt

So-called on account of its curious, pouch-shaped seed pods, shepherd's purse is a domestic remedy of long standing for stopping both internal and external bleeding. During World War I the Germans used an extract of shepherd's purse for staunching wounds. The young leaves have a cress-like flavour and were a common spring vegetable.

HABITAT Native to Europe and established worldwide in temperate zones. A common weed found in fields, gardens, and on roadsides and waste ground.

DESCRIPTION Annual with a basal rosette of grey-green, dandelion-like leaves and slender stems that are sparsely branched. The smaller stem leaves are arrow-shaped. Small, white inconspicuous flowers bloom for most of the year at the end of the flowering stems, and are followed by flattened triangular seed pods.

Skullcap

Scutellaria latifolia spp.

Labiatae

Mad-dog weed

Skullcap, as the name suggests, is beneficial for tension headaches as it has a soothing effect on the nervous system. It was once reputed to cure rabies, hence its country name.

HABITAT Native to Canada and the northern and eastern USA. Grows in wet meadows and near rivers and lakes. A related species *Scutellaria galericulata* is common in wet places in the UK.

DESCRIPTION Perennial with square, slender stems from 15–45cm(6–18in) and opposite, ovate leaves with serrated edges that taper to a point. From mid-summer to early autumn pairs of two-lipped, pouched, bright blue flowers bloom in the leaf axils.

Skunk Cabbage

Symplocarpus foetidus

Araceae

The roots of this disagreeable-smelling plant are a traditional folk remedy for tight coughs, bronchitis and catarrh. Skunk cabbage acts as a mild sedative and has been employed to treat nervous disorders. One Native American tribe inhaled the crushed leaves to ease headaches.

HABITAT Native to swampy areas of the eastern USA and westwards to Iowa.

DESCRIPTION Perennial with tuberous, fleshy rootstock that sends up a sheathed, fleshy, oval spike that bears small, purple flowers from late winter to early spring, before the leaves appear. The plant grows to 40cm(16in) and bears heart-shaped, thick-stalked leaves that resemble those of the cabbage. The whole plant gives off a fetid, unpleasant smell.

Slippery Elm

Ulmus fulva

Ulmaceae

Indian elm, moose elm

The valuable healing properties of the moist inner bark of the Indian elm have long been known to native Americans. Slippery elm is both a nourishing food, especially during convalescence, and a soothing medicine for stomach ulcers and gastric upsets.

HABITAT Native North American tree growing in moist woods and along streams from southern Canada southwards to Florida and Texas. Also grown as an ornamental.

DESCRIPTION Deciduous tree to 15m(50ft) with ridged, dark brown bark and whitish, aromatic inner bark. The leaf buds are covered in thick yellowish felt. The roughish dark green leaves are olbong to obovate and have serrated edges. Dense clusters of inconspicuous flowers appear in spring.

Soapwort
Saponaria officinalis

Caryophyllaceae
Fullers' herb, latherwort

Soapwort yields a gentle lather when boiled in water, which is suitable for cleaning old and delicate materials. In the days before chemical detergents, the plant was grown around wool mills to clean or 'full' woollen cloth. Medicinally, a soapwort lotion is soothing for sore, irritated skin.

HABITAT Native to western Asia. Naturalized in Europe and eastern North America. Common on roadsides, railway embankments, and waste ground.

DESCRIPTION Perennial with a single, thick, slightly branched stem to 80cm(32in), and oval leaves that clasp the stem and narrow to a point. From mid-summer to early autumn clusters of large pale pink flowers with five petals and ten stamens grow at the top of the stem.

Solomon's Seal
Polygonatum multiflorum

Liliaceae
Sealwort, dropberry

The scarred root of this plant reputedly bears the seal of Solomon, a noted herbalist. Native American women drank the root tea for menstrual problems and the fresh root was applied to bruises 'gotten by fals or women's wilfulness in stumbling upon their hastie husband's fists' (Gerard).

HABITAT Native to northern Europe and eastwards to Siberia and Asia. Naturalized in eastern North America. Grows wild in woods and shady places. Also cultivated as a garden plant.

DESCRIPTION Perennial with a thick, horizontal rootstock bearing circular scars. The erect stem inclines towards the tip and grows to 60cm(2ft). The leaves are elliptic, dark green and marked with numerous parallel veins. From spring to early summer drooping clusters of tubular, greenish-white, fragrant flowers appear that grow to one side.

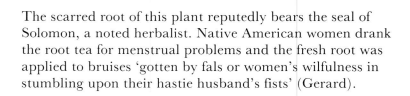

Sorrel

Rumex acetosa and spp.

Polygonaceae
Common sorrel, sour sauce

The common name of this herb is derived from the old French *surele*, meaning sour, and sorrel leaves are well known for their acidity. They make excellent soups and sauces, and have been used in cooking since the time of the ancient Egyptians. The Romans served sorrel to balance the richness of their food, and during the Middle Ages sorrel was one of the most common kitchen-garden herbs. Old English recipes recommend a sour green sauce based on sorrel with roast goose or pork, and sorrel sauce is traditionally served with salmon. Cultivated French sorrel has a better flavour than common sorrel and in France, sorrel soup is a classic dish. The acid juice of sorrel was once used to curdle milk and the salts, once sold as 'essential salt of lemons' have stain-removing properties.

Culpeper considered sorrel beneficial for 'agues pestilential or choleric', and the leaves were made into a cooling drink to bring down the temperature in fevers until the early part of this century. Sorrel juice, mixed with vinegar and honey, was also prescribed for sore throats. Fresh sorrel contains vitamin C and so was beneficial in cases of scurvy. Today, sorrel is rarely used medicinally.

CAUTION Sorrel contains oxalic acid salts and in large doses it can cause serious kidney damage. Avoid sorrel if you suffer from kidney disease, arthritis, or rheumatism.

HABITAT Native to Europe, particularly the UK. Introduced and naturalized in North America. Grows wild in meadows and grassland, along roadsides, and in open woods, on moist, loamy soils rich in nitrogen.

DESCRIPTION Perennial member of the dock family with slender green stems that may be tinged with red from 40–100cm(20–39in). The thick, tapering, dark green leaves resemble spinach. They are arrow-shaped at the base with rounded lobes, and decrease in size becoming more oblong towards the top of the stalk. Small, reddish-brown or reddish-green flowers grow in thin spikes at the tips of the stems from early to late summer. Common sorrel is closely related to the cultivated French sorrel *Rumex scutatus*, which has fleshier, more heart-shaped leaves.

GROWING TIPS Sow seed in mid-spring in a rich soil in a sunny, preferably sheltered position. The leaves are ready for harvesting after about four months.

Southernwood

Artemisia abrotanum

Compositae

Lad's love, *Garde-robe* (Fr)

In rural areas, young men not only considered southernwood an aphrodisiac but also employed the herb to speed up the growth of facial hair. The strong scent of the herb repels moths and sprays were commonly laid amongst clothes, hence its French name, *garde-robe* (clothes-preserver).

HABITAT Native to southern Europe, especially Spain and Italy. Naturalized in temperate zones, including the eastern USA. Grown as a garden ornamental but may not flower in cooler northern climates.

DESCRIPTION Strong, sharp-smelling bushy perennial and member of the wormwood family. The branching stems grow from 90–150cm(3–5ft) and bear grey-green, often downy, leaves that are finely divided and feathery. Loose clusters of small, inconspicuous, yellowish-white flowers appear from late summer to early autumn.

Squaw Vine

Mitchella repens

Rubiaceae

Partridgeberry

Squaw vine is a native American remedy of long standing and a tea was taken during the final stages of pregnancy to facilitate childbirth. Herbalists still recommend squaw vine, often in combination with raspberry leaves, to tone and strengthen the uterus before birth.

HABITAT Native to North America from Nova Scotia southwards to Florida and Texas. Grows in forests and woodland, around the bottom of trees and tree stumps.

DESCRIPTION Trailing evergreen with rooting stems up to 1m(3ft) in length. The dark green leaves are opposite and resemble those of clover with shiny upper surfaces. Tubular white flowers grow in pairs from early to mid-summer and are followed by a scarlet, many-seeded berry.

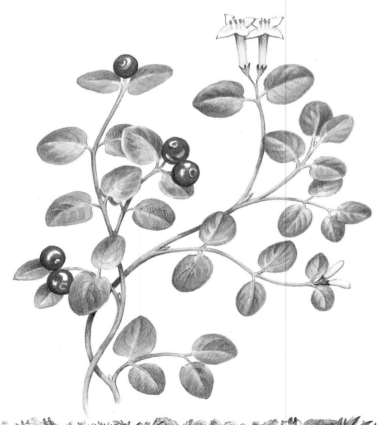

Stone Root
Collinsonia canadensis

Labiatae
Horseweed

As the common name suggests, the hard root of this herb acts on the urinary system and is traditionally employed to ease the passing of urinary stones. Horseweed indicates its former use in veterinary medicine.

HABITAT Native to North America, in moist woods, from Quebec westwards to Wisconsin and southwards to Florida.

DESCRIPTION Unpleasant smelling perennial. The hard, brownish-grey, knobbly rhizome sends up a four-sided stem from 30–120cm(1–4ft) with opposite, ovate leaves that are heart-shaped at the base and have serrated edges. From July to September large, two-lipped greenish-yellow flowers grow in a loose terminal spike.

Strawberry, Wild
Fragaria vesca

Rosaceae
Wood strawberry

In Europe, wild strawberries have been gathered from the woods since at least the tenth century. The cultivated strawberry was introduced to Europe from the USA in the early part of the seventeenth century. Medicinally, a tea of the leaves was drunk for diarrhoea and the berries were considered invaluable for feverish conditions and gout. Fresh strawberries remove discolorations from the teeth.

HABITAT Native to Europe, eastern North America, and western Asia. Found in clearings in woods and forests, and on dry grassland in shady spots.

DESCRIPTION Perennial from 15–25cm(6–10in) on runners. Resembles a garden strawberry in minature. The pale green stems are covered with soft hairs and the leaves are divided into three coarsely toothed leaflets. Small white flowers bloom from mid-spring to mid-summer followed by small, sweet, scarlet fruit.

Summer Savory

Satureia hortensis

Labiatae

In Europe, the leaves of both summer and winter savory were traditionally used to flavour food, long before the introduction of spices from India and the Far East. Savory was popular with the ancient Romans who pounded it up with vinegar to make a sauce for roast meat. They introduced the herb to England and the Saxons named it savory, after its biting, pungent flavour. Savory was well known to Shakespeare who refers to the herb in *The Winter's Tale*, while in Tudor England, winter savory shrubs were a common feature in knot gardens as well as kitchen gardens. In the seventeenth century, savory was traditionally served with trout, and mixed with breadcrumbs as a coating for both fish and meat. In modern cookery, summer savory is considered superior to winter savory. Its pungent, peppery flavour complements sausages and stuffings, and it is one of the traditional seasonings for Italian salami. In Germany, savory is the traditional flavouring for beans, and helps to make them more digestible.

The genus *Satureia* means belonging to the satyrs. According to Greek mythology, satyrs were rather lascivious, horned creatures with cloven hoofs who inhabited the forests and were fond of chasing nymphs. This legendary association probably gave rise to summer savory's reputation as an aphrodisiac and also goes some way towards explaining the herb's continued popularity in cooking. Both savories, however, were used medicinally as digestive herbs and were considered warming to the stomach and helpful for flatulence and colic. Culpeper assigned savory to the planet Mercury, associated with the respiratory system, and recommended summer savory for asthma and other chest complaints.

HABITAT Native to the Mediterranean and introduced to the UK and North America. Widely cultivated as a culinary herb.

DESCRIPTION Very aromatic annual from 30–45cm(12–18in). The erect, branching stems are covered with fine hairs and bear pairs of oblong, pointed leaves with a purplish tinge. Small, two-lipped white to rose pink flowers bloom in groups of three to six in the upper leaf axils from late summer to mid-autumn. Winter savory (*Satureia montana*), a close relative, is a hardy perennial. It is bushier, woody at the base, and has a stronger scent than summer savory. The leaves of winter savory are glossy, dark green and lance-shaped, and the white, purple-spotted flowers grow in terminal spikes.

GROWING TIPS Sow summer savory seeds in spring in a sunny position in ordinary garden soil. Thin out to 25cm(10in) and keep well watered during hot, dry weather.

Sunflower

Helianthus annuus

Compositae

The botanical name *Helianthus* means flower (*anthos*) of the Sun (*helios*), a reference to the round yellow heads that resemble the sun's disk surrounded by rays. The flower heads are also supposed to rotate so that they always turn towards the sun, hence sunflower's Spanish and French names *girasol* and *tournesol*. In ancient Peru, where the flower is thought to have originated, the sun-worshipping Incas regarded the sunflower as the emblem of their sun god. Sunflower headdresses were worn by the Inca priestesses and flowers wrought in gold adorned the Inca temples of the sun.

Sunflower seeds yield a pale yellow oil that has a high percentage of unsaturated fats. Sunflower oil has a milder taste than olive oil, and it is thought to be healthier for the arteries than butter on account of its low saturated fat content. In recent years, sunflower oil margerine has become a popular alternative to butter. In Spain sunflower seeds, known as *pipas* (pips), are roasted in their shells and enjoyed as a snack. They are rich in Vitamins B_1, B_3, and B_6 and are also made into a nutritious spread, available from health food stores. All parts of the sunflower are useful: the leaves make good cattle fodder, while the fibrous stems were once used to make paper. The young flower buds can also be boiled and eaten like artichokes.

Medicinally, sunflower seeds have expectorant and diuretic properties and were once considered beneficial for colds, coughs and bronchitis. The leaves and flowers, which have weak insecticidal properties, were thought to offer some protection against malaria, and a poultice of the fresh leaves was a Russian folk remedy for fevers.

HABITAT Native to Central America, probably originating in Peru. Introduced into North America, the Mediterranean, eastern Europe, and the USSR. Widespread commercial cultivation in countries including Italy, the USA, Hungary, Rumania, and Argentina. Grown as a garden ornamental.

DESCRIPTION Tall, striking annual with a stout, rough, hairy stem from 1–3m(3–10ft). The rough-textured leaves are broad with coarsely serrated edges and have prominent veins. The familiar bright yellow flowers have honeycomb-like brownish centres composed of small tubular flowers that ripen into the familiar pale greyish seeds.

GROWING TIPS Sow seeds in boxes under glass and transfer seedlings to pots. Harden off and plant out in deep, well-manured soil 60cm(2ft) apart with a tall stick for support. Choose a sunny position with shelter from strong winds.

Sweet Cicely

Myrrhis odorata

Umbelliferae

British myrrh, sweet fern, sweet chervil

The plant's common name reflects its sweet, almost sugary, smell and taste which has been likened to anise or liquorice. Sweet cicely's generic botanical name *Myrrhis* is derived from the greek for perfume, while *odorata* means fragrant. Sweet cicely retains its foliage for most of the year – one of the principal reasons for its popularity as a cottage garden herb in seventeenth-century England. The sugary-tasting leaves have an anise-like taste, and they are traditionally cooked with tart fruits, such as rhubarb and gooseberries and used to flavour fruit salads and fruit pies. Some recipes for stewed fruit dishes advocate halving the quantity of sugar called for when using sweet cicely. The fresh leaves impart their own sweetness and are, therefore, helpful for diabetics and those on low-sugar diets. Sweet cicely leaves are also traditional in salads. According to Gerard, sweet cicely leaves are 'exceedingly good, holsome, and pleasant among other sallade herbes, giving the taste of anise seed unto the rest'. The seeds can be substituted for caraway seeds in cakes and biscuits.

Sweet cicely appears to have been used medicinally since Roman times. Today, it is used exclusively in cooking. An infusion of the herb was once recommended for flatulence and coughs, and it was an ingredient of wound-healing ointments. The roots have a mild antiseptic action and were reputed to cure the bites of mad dogs and snakes. They were also steeped in brandy or wine and taken morning and evening as a remedy for consumption. As a medicinal herb, however, sweet cicely, described by old herbalists as – 'so harmless you cannot use it amiss' – does not appear to have made much of an impression.

HABITAT Native to Europe, including northern England and Scotland. Naturalized in North America. Found in grassy places, hedgerows and on wood edges, often in hilly regions. Prefers shade.

DESCRIPTION Perennial to 1m(3ft) with a strong, sweet scent, reminiscent of anise. The stout, branching stem is grooved and hairy, and bears large, aromatic fern-like leaves that are bright green above and paler beneath. The leaves are subdivided into narrow, toothed leaflets, and the stem leaves are sheathed. From mid-spring to early summer, umbels of numerous white flowers appear and are followed by large, brown, ridged seeds.

GROWING TIPS Sow in early spring or autumn in a shady position in moist, well-drained soil. Germination may be slow. Sweet cicely may also be propagated by dividing the roots in autumn.

Sweet Violet

Viola odorata

Violaceae

The violet genus is reputedly named in honour of Io, one of Zeus' many lovers. According to Greek legend, Zeus turned her into a white heifer to that she would escape the wrath of his wife Hera. Violets then materialized at her feet so that she would have enough to eat. To the ancient Celts, the violet was a beauty aid, and Culpeper assigned the flower to the planetary rulership of Venus. In the language of flowers, the violet signifies modesty as well as fidelity, and posies of violets were reputedly exchanged between Napoleon Bonaparte and Josephine. Napoleon later adopted the flower as the emblem of the Imperial Napoleonic party. In southern France, violets were once offered as prizes for love poetry, possibly due to their earlier association in Greek myth with Orpheus, the heroic Greek poet. They are also used both to colour and flavour an intensely sweet French liqueur called *parfait amour*.

Violets have long been associated with calmness and sleep. The Athenians made a sleeping potion from violets and the flowers were also thought to calm anger. Wearing violets around the head was an old folk remedy for curing dizziness, and Culpeper claimed that the violet 'easeth pains in the head caused thru' want of sleep'. Gerard, too, prescribed a syrup of violets for insomnia and headaches, as well as for sore throats. Modern herbalists value the expectorant properties of the leaves and flowers, and prescribe them for coughs, bronchitis and catarrh. A series of tests carried out in the 1960s showed that an extract of violet leaves inhibited the growth of tumours in mice.

Violets have been grown for their sweet scent for over 2000 years, and violet water and perfume were particularly popular in Victorian England. Today, confectioners use crystallized violets to decorate cakes, pastries, and chocolates. In France, veal dishes were traditionally garnished with violet petals. Both flowers and leaves are rich in vitamins A and C.

HABITAT Native to Europe, North Africa, and Asia. Introduced and naturalized in temperate zones, including North America. Found in hedgebanks, wood clearings, and on wood edges, especially in moist, chalky soils. Cultivated commercially.

DESCRIPTION Fragrant, low-growing perennial to 15cm(6in) with dark green kidney- or heart-shaped leaves that grow on long footstalks. The leaves are downy beneath and the edges are scalloped. From early to mid-spring, pretty, sweet-scented, drooping flowers bloom singly. They have five petals, the lower one spurred, and the colour varies from deep purple to lilac, pinkish-lilac, and even white.

Tansy

Tanacetum vulgare

Compositae

Buttons, bachelor's buttons

The common name of this plant is thought to be derived from the Greek *athanaton* meaning deathless, probably in view of its enduring flowers. Legend has it that Ganymede, the beautiful cup-bearer to the Greek gods, drank a potion of the blossoms to secure his immortality. A more prosaic explanation for the connection with immortality is the ancient custom of laying sprigs of tansy over corpses to help protect them from decay. Tansy has insect-repellant and preservative properties, and it was once customary to rub the fresh herb on joints of meat to keep off flies.

In England during the sixteenth century, after a Lenten diet of salt fish, young tansy leaves were traditionally made into Easter puddings and cakes, and eaten with fried eggs. The custom of eating sharp-tasting tansy may have been in honour of the bitter herbs eaten by the Jews at Passover. However, since tansy effectively expels worms from the body, the practice may have had a beneficial effect on the digestive system after so much salted food.

During the sixteenth and seventeenth centuries, fresh tansy was strewn around the home to mask unpleasant smells and keep out flies. At the coronation of King James II, quantities of deodorizing tansy were laid along the pathway to the throne. Tansy was once considered a beauty aid and made into a skin-whitening complexion milk. Culpeper claimed that garden tansy would 'pleasure women with child', and assigned tansies to the planetary rulership of Venus. Native Americans were also aware of tansy's reputation as a fertility agent and used a poultice of the fresh leaves to encourage conception. In large doses, however, tansy is toxic and can induce abortion. Herbalists consider small doses of tansy useful for expelling roundworms and threadworms, and they may suggest a tansy wash for acne and itchy skin infections.

HABITAT Native to Europe and Asia. Introduced and naturalized in the north-eastern USA from Nova Scotia westwards to Minnesota and southwards to Missouri. Found in hedgerows, along roadsides and on waste ground.

DESCRIPTION Straggling perennial with erect, leafy stems from 60–90cm(2–3ft). The finely cut, alternate leaves are fern-like and the leaflets are deeply lobed and toothed. When brushed they give off a camphor-like smell. From mid-summer to early autumn, loose clusters of button-like flower heads appear that are an attractive golden yellow.

Tarragon

Artemisia dracunculus

Compositae

French tarragon, 'true' French tarragon

Tarragon's specific botanical name *dracunculus*, from the Greek *drakon*, means little dragon, and is probably a reference to the plant's serpentine root system. According to medieval folklore, plants with coiled roots were widely believed to cure the bites of venomous snakes. The Romans thought tarragon would ward off exhaustion and this belief persisted through the Middle Ages when it was customary for pilgrims to place fresh sprigs inside their boots before starting out. The root was once a popular cure for toothache, and the fresh leaves do, in fact, produce a slight numbness of the mouth. Gerard declared tarragon to be 'highly cordial and friend to the head, heart and liver'.

Today, tarragon is no longer used medicinally. It is, however, one of the most important of European culinary herbs and considered indispensable in classic French cooking. Tarragon has an unusual, rather tart flavour that can be overpowering if added too liberally. It is usually encountered in the form of tarragon vinegar, in tarragon mustards, and in the *fines herbes* mixture for omelettes. Tarragon goes particularly well with egg dishes, as well as fish and chicken, and fresh tarragon or tarragon vinegar are essential for such sauces as *béarnaise*, *hollandaise*, and *tartare*. When dried, tarragon tends to lose its flavour. Russian tarragon has a coarser, more pungent taste than French tarragon, but both types are said to promote a good appetite.

HABITAT Native to southern Europe. Introduced elsewhere as a garden herb and cultivated commercially in Europe, Asia, and the USA. Russian tarragon *Artemisia dracunculoides*, a closely related plant, is a native of Siberia and the Caspian Sea.

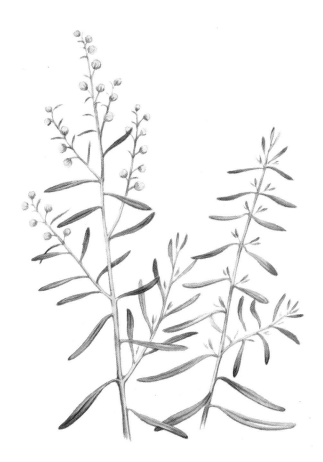

DESCRIPTION Bushy, aromatic perennial from 60–90cm(2–3ft) that is similar in appearance to wormwood and a member of the same family. The slender stems bear smooth, dark, shiny leaves. They are narrow and linear in shape and widely spaced along the stem. From mid- to late summer, small globular flowers appear that are greyish-green or greenish white, and woolly. French tarragon, however, will only flower in warm climates. Russian tarragon is a taller, coarser plant with roughish, pale green leaves.

GROWING TIPS 'True' French tarragon must be started from cuttings or seedlings as the seed always produces the Russian variety. Plant out in spring in well-drained soil in a sunny, sheltered position. Protect from wind and frost during winter and do not allow the soil to become wet. The herb may also be grown indoors in pots.

Thuja

Thuja occidentalis

Cupressaceae

Northern white cedar, Tree of life

Thuja is thought to be derived from the Greek meaning 'to sacrifice', or possibly 'to fumigate', since it was apparently customary in ancient times to burn the sweet-scented wood during sacrificial rites. *Occidentalis* means western, to differentiate it from the Chinese or eastern thuja, *Thuja orientalis*. The thuja was introduced into France from Canada and planted in the grounds of the royal palace at Fontainebleau. It reached England around the middle of the sixteenth century. In its native Canada, thuja branches were once used to make brooms, while in more recent times the pliable and durable softwood has been employed for fencing.

Thuja's medicinal action is principally due to the presence of a volatile oil, thujone. This substance acts on the smooth muscles of the body, such as those of the uterus, and Native Americans drank a tea of the inner bark to promote menstruation. An infusion of the twigs is also said to be helpful in cases of incontinence due to poor muscle tone. Thuja has an expectorant and diuretic action and herbalists may prescribe it for bronchitis and catarrh. Externally, a wash of the herb is considered beneficial for such skin infections as impetigo, and also for warts. Homeopaths, too, value the medicinal properties of thuja and recommend it for body odour, morning headaches and warts.

CAUTION Thuja must only be taken under the supervision of a qualified practitioner as thujone is toxic. Avoid during pregnancy.

HABITAT Native to North America from Quebec southwards to North Carolina. Grows along the banks of streams and rivers, and in moist places. Introduced into Europe and the UK as an ornamental tree in gardens and parks.

DESCRIPTION Conifer that can reach 21m(70ft) but in the UK rarely exceeds 10m(30ft). The tree has a rather ragged conical crown, yet a graceful appearance. The trunk is covered in a light brown outer bark that is composed of long, flaking strips. The shortish branches bear opposite pairs of bright green, mildly fragrant leaves that are composed of overlapping scales. The surface is rough in texture due to a raised gland on each leaf. Minute greenish-yellow flowers bloom at the tips of the branches from mid-spring to mid-summer and are followed by small pale green cones that ripen to light chestnut.

Thyme

Thymus vulgaris

Labiatae

Common thyme, garden thyme

Thymus has two possible derivations: from the Greek word for courage, or from a term meaning to cleanse or fumigate. In the Age of Chivalry thyme motifs were embroidered on knights' scarves to inspire courage before a jousting tournament. Sprigs of the herb were also burned indoors to cleanse the air, and were thought to offer protection from the plague. The herb was also associated with death: thyme was once planted on graves in Wales and sprigs were carried at funerals of the members of a British secret benevolent society known as the Oddfellows. According to a curious old superstition, planting a bed of thyme in the garden would either bring fairies to the home or enable one to catch sight of them.

Thymol, the essential oil present in thyme, is strongly antibacterial, hence its reputation as a herbal disinfectant. Thyme tea is a traditional remedy for gastro-intestinal complaints and the oil was once taken to expel intestinal parasites, particularly hookworm. Thyme also has antispasmodic properties which make it an effective remedy for sore throats, irritable coughs, and bronchitis. A thyme mouthwash is also helpful for gum infections. Externally, thyme oil was used as an antiseptic during World War I.

Thyme is traditionally included in sausages, meat loaf, terrines and stuffing mixtures, both for its preservative qualities as well as its savoury taste. It is an important herb in southern French, Greek, Creole and Cajun cuisines.

HABITAT Native to the western Mediterranean and southern Italy. Introduced elsewhere and widely cultivated, especially in Hungary and Germany. Found on dry, rocky, or well-drained soils.

DESCRIPTION Perennial that may be grown as an annual in cold climates. Bushy herb with several, many branched, wooded stems that grows from 10–30cm(4–12in) with strongly aromatic leaves. These are small, narrow, and elliptical to lance-shaped with greyish-green uppers and downy undersides. From early to mid-summer whorls of lilac to pink, tubular, lipped flowers grow in clusters at the tips of the branches. Several varieties of thyme are available including broad-leaved, narrow-leaved, variegated and lemon thyme.

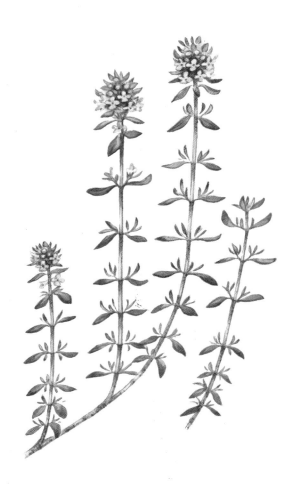

GROWING TIPS Sow seed indoors in the warmth, or propagate from cuttings. Plant out seedlings in a sunny, sheltered position in light, very well-drained soil. Thyme prefers poor, fairly rocky soil.

Valerian

Valeriana officinalis

Valerianaceae

Common valerian, garden heliotrope

In medieval times valerian was considered a cure-all, and one suggested origin of its name is the Latin verb *valere*, meaning to be well. Both the common valerian and marsh valerian *Valeriana dioica* were employed medicinally by the early Arabian physicians, and one offensive-smelling variety was known to the ancient Greek herbalists as *phu*. Valerian soon acquired a reputation as a cure for epilepsy, due to the valuable antispasmodic properties of the root, and it was extensively employed from the mid-sixteenth century to treat convulsions and other nervous disorders. Valerian is a very effective natural tranquillizer and from the early nineteenth century to the mid-twentieth century it was an official drug in the USA. Valepotriates, the active ingredients of valerian root, have been shown to calm the central nervous system and modern herbalists consider the herb a valuable remedy for nervous anxiety and insomnia. The herb or its derivatives can be found in several herbal sedatives and sleeping preparations, particularly in Germany, and it is reputed to be helpful for pre-flight nerves.

Valerian root also has a tranquillizing effect on animals. Rat-catchers once used valerian in their traps, and the legendary Pied Piper probably lured rats away from Hamelin using the scent of the valerian roots stuffed in his pockets. Cats, too, are said to become strangely intoxicated by the scent of valerian, and will roll in any plant with bruised or damaged leaves. The Anglo-Saxons ate valerian in salads, considering it both a food and a medicine, and as late as the seventeenth century, country folk were very partial to the fresh root, which they called Setewale, in soups and stews. Valerian oil was once used to perfume soap, and to give added flavour to tobacco.

HABITAT Native to Europe and western Asia. Naturalized in North America, from New England southwards to New Jersey. Found in rough meadowland, on moist grassland, along the banks of streams and ditches and sometimes on roadsides.

DESCRIPTION Tall, conspicuous, rather fetid smelling perennial from 90–120cm(3–4ft). The single, grooved stem is hairy towards the base and bears slender horizontal branches and pairs of dark green, pinnate leaves. They are joined at the base and are ovate to lance-shaped with uneven, ascending indentations. The upper surface of the leaves is veined and softly hairy. From early to late summer two or more pairs of flowering stems bear loose clusters of palest pink to white, five-petalled flowers that have a slight fragrance.

Verbena, Lemon

Aloysia triphylla

Verbenaceae

Lemon verbena was discovered growing wild in Chile and Argentina by Spanish colonists, who brought it back to Europe on account of its pronounced lemon scent. At banquets lemon verbena scented the water in finger bowls, and the fresh leaves were used as a perfumed body rub after bathing. Later, the essential oil was extracted from the leaves and employed in perfumery, soap and bath essences. The fragrance was apparently popular with ladies in the Deep South: it was the chosen perfume of Scarlet O'Hara's mother in *Gone with the Wind*. Today, lemon grass is commonly substituted. Dried lemon verbena is still popular in pot pourris and can be added to fragrant herbal sachets for cupboards and drawers.

Lemon verbena is more usually encountered in the form of a tisane. This delicate-flavoured tea has long been popular in Spain, and in summer it is particularly refreshing taken iced with the addition of a sprig of fresh mint. Hot lemon verbena is considered to have both sedative and digestive properties. It is a traditional folk remedy for indigestion and flatulence, and is reputed to soothe the nerves and ease palpitations. The young leaves also add a lemon tang to summer fruit drinks and fruit salads, and may be substituted for lemon rind in sweet sauces. The fresh leaves are tough, so remove them before serving and use the herb sparingly, as some find its taste rather soapy.

HABITAT Native to Chile and Argentina, and widespread in tropical countries. Introduced into temperate zones, and cultivated commercially in France and North Africa. Popularly grown indoors in pots.

DESCRIPTION Lemon-scented, woody, deciduous shrub that reaches 3m(10ft) in warm climates, but rarely grows higher than 1.5m(5ft) in cooler countries. The rough-textured branches bear fragrant, narrow, lance-shaped leaves that are arranged in whorls of three. They are pale green with a prominent mid-rib and oil glands are visible on the undersides. From late summer slender spikes of numerous, tiny pale lavender flowers bloom towards the ends of the branches.

GROWING TIPS Sow seeds, if available, or propagate from cuttings taken in summer. Plant in a light, well-drained soil in a very sheltered, sunny position as the plant is easily damaged by cold and wind. Cut back in winter and cover the base with straw. Lemon verbena is often grown in a container and brought indoors during cold weather. In North America it is usually regarded as a house plant.

Vervain

Verbena officinalis

Verbenaceae

Herb of Grace, holy herb, enchanter's plant, herb of
Venus

The genus *Verbena* means 'holy bough' and vervain, the
enchanter's plant, has a long association with mysticism and
magic. The Romans employed vervain as an altar plant, and
the ancient Egyptians dedicated it to the sorceress-goddess
Isis. In Celtic Britain, the Druids included the herb in the
purifying or 'lustral' water they used for sacrifices, and it was
widely employed for sacred rituals. Vervain is thought to be
a name of Celtic origin, meaning a stone-expeller, and it was
an old herbal remedy for urinary stones and gravel. With the
emergence of Christianity, vervain became associated with
the crucifixion and legend has it that vervain stemmed the
bleeding from Christ's wounds. At one time it was customary
to bless the herb before picking it.

Vervain's legendary connection with the crucifixion
assured its reputation as a potent healer, and the leaves were
applied to cuts and wounds. In medieval times, people wore
necklaces of the fresh plant as lucky charms and believed
that vervain would protect them from headaches and
snakebites. Vervain was also known as the herb of Venus
and it was popularly made into love charms and potions. In
seventeenth-century England, Culpeper, mindful of its
association with the goddess of love, prescribed vervain for
'pain in the secret parts'. Modern herbalists, building on the
experience of their superstitious medieval counterparts, also
consider vervain helpful for headaches, particularly
migraine-type headaches accompanied by nausea. The herb
is said to have a strengthening effect on the nervous system
and is often recommended for tension, depression and
nervous exhaustion. A decocotion of vervain added to the
bathwater is a pleasant way of easing tension.

CAUTION Vervain can act specifically on the uterus so
avoid this herb during pregnancy.

HABITAT Native to Europe, particularly the Mediterranean
region, and naturalized in North America. Grows on
roadsides, rough pastures and on waste ground. Prefers
chalky soils.

DESCRIPTION Perennial with a sparsely leaved, slender,
angular stem from 30–90cm(1–3ft). The oblong, ovate leaves
are opposite, ovate and usually deeply lobed. The upper
leaves clasp the stem and are covered in short hairs; the
lower are stalked. Tiny white, lilac-tinged flowers appear at
the tips of the long, flowering stalks throughout the summer
months. They have five petals and no scent.

Virginia Snakeroot
Aristolochia serpentaria

Aristolochiaceae
Serpentary, birthwort

The genus name *Aristolochia* is derived from the Greek *aristos*, meaning finest, and *locheia*, meaning delivery. The ancient Greek herbalists thought that plants belonging to this genus facilitated childbirth, hence the common name, birthwort. This particular species, however, was not employed during the final stages of pregnancy, although it was used to regulate the menstrual cycle.

Virginia snakeroot's once considerable reputation was founded on the belief that it would cure rattlesnake and other poisonous bites and stings. It is not clear how this property came to be associated with the plant: some sources maintain that early Egyptian snake charmers employed the roots of a related species to paralyze the mouths of their snakes before performing dangerous tricks. Another possibility is that the unusual, low-growing, S-shaped flowers resemble snakes. Native American Indian tribes were the first to apply the chewed root to snake bites, after first sucking out the venom. Early American settlers took note of this practice and virginia snakeroot was introduced into European medicine from the mid-sixteenth century. The root continued to be regarded as one of the foremost cures for snake bites and mad dog bites as late as the mid-eighteenth century.

Today, virginia snakeroot is not widely employed in herbal medicine. Small doses are said to stimulate the appetite and aid the digestion but large doeses can result in vomiting and intense griping pains. One of the active principles in the root is an alkaloid which, taken in sufficient quantities, can result in severe internal damage, leading to coma and even death.

HABITAT Native to North America from the eastern and central USA southwards. Grows in shady woods in rich, well-drained soil.

DESCRIPTION Perennial with erect, wavy stems to 60cm(2ft) rising from a horizontal rhizome that sends out numerous slender roots. The foliage is rather sparse and composed of alternate, heart-shaped leaves that taper to a point. In early summer, dull purplish-brown, tubular flowers appear on short scaly stalks from the base of the stem, and may give off an unpleasant scent. The drooping flowers grow very low and may touch the ground.

GROWING TIPS Several species of *Aristolochia*, often known as 'Dutchman's pipe' make unusual and attractive garden plants, and some are climbers. They can be grown from seed but require long germination in the warmth. Virginia snakeroot can be propagated by root division but is slow to become established. The plant prefers fertile, well-drained soil and partial shade.

Walnut

Juglans regia, Juglans nigra

Juglandaceae

Common walnut, English or Persian walnut

The walnut's botanical name, *Juglans*, is from the Latin for Jupiter's acorn, since walnuts were supposedly eaten by the Greek gods. The walnut's association with Jupiter, the philandering king of the gods, has survived in folk medicine: the green outer shell of the walnut is reputed to increase virility.

The ancient Romans extracted the brown stain from walnut husks for use as a hair dye, and in the seventeenth century, and until the early part of this century, hair colouring preparations contained walnut extract. In recent years interest in walnut's cosmetic properties has been rekindled, owing to the harsh effects of many chemical hair dyes. Another association between walnuts and the head was put forward by adherents of the Doctrine of Signatures. They maintained that the husk was the same shape as the head and recommended it for head wounds, while the brain-like edible kernel would 'comfort the brain and head mightily'. Modern herbalists occasionally employ walnut leaves for treating skin problems, but the nuts are no longer used medicinally.

In the kitchen, walnut oil is particularly good in salad dressings and in the UK, where the nuts rarely ripen, the green fruits are suitable for pickling. A strong infusion of walnut leaves is also said to deter ants. A sign depicting a walnut tree traditionally hung outside a cabinet maker's workshop.

HABITAT The common walnut *Juglans regia* is probably native to Iran but extends westwards to the Balkan Mountains and eastwards to China. Introduced and found wild in open woodland in Europe and southern and central England. Widely cultivated in warm climates, especially Spain, and common in parks and gardens. The black walnut *Juglans nigra* is native to the Appalachian Mountains of North America.

DESCRIPTION The common walnut is a large, attractive, deciduous tree with spreading boughs and a wide crown that grows from 23–25m(74–80ft). The massive trunk is covered in smooth grey to silvery grey slabs of bark with deep fissures. The large, dull green leaves are pinnate in form with approximately seven to nine leaflets and are strongly aromatic. In shape they are ovate with a pointed tip, smooth edges, and prominent mid-rib. In spring to early summer drooping male catkins and inconspicuous female flowers appear. These are followed by globular fruits composed of a green outer casing that envelops the familiar nut with its wrinkled light brown husk. The black walnut has darker, more deeply ridged bark than the common walnut. The pinnate leaves usually have about 15 leaflets and serrated edges.

Watercress

Nasturtium officinale

Cruciferae

Scurvy grass

From the earliest times, watercress has been valued as both a food and a medicine. The plant is rich in vitamins and minerals, particularly vitamin C and iron, and is one of the oldest remedies for preventing or curing scurvy, hence its country name, scurvy grass. Hippocrates, who died in 377 BC, considered watercress a digestive stimulant and also recommended it for coughs. The fresh plant, especially the juice, is an appetite stimulant and was once considered an effective remedy for tuberculosis and asthma. Herbalists still recommend watercress for catarrh and bronchitis, and in folk medicine a soothing cough mixture is prepared from fresh watercress and honey. Watercress is an excellent internal cleanser and aids the elimination of excess fluid from the body. It is helpful for mild digestive disorders and skin problems – in the seventeenth century Culpeper prescribed a watercress lotion for clearing up spots and pimples.

On account of its hot, pungent taste, watercress was named *Nasturtium*, from two Latin words meaning twisting or wrinkling up of the nose. For culinary use, it is better to buy commercially grown watercress, which has been grown in prepared beds fed by clean, running water. The wild plant may grow in still water of questionable quality and may carry a deadly parasite, the liver fluke. Watercress picked from stretches of contaminated water was once a common source of typhoid infection. Raw watercress not only makes a good winter salad vegetable but is also said to strengthen the gums. It may also be used instead of parsley in sauces for fish. Excessive consumption of watercress, however, may lead to kidney problems, and large doses are purgative.

HABITAT Native to Europe. Introduced and naturalized in North America and throughout the world. Found in ditches, at the sides of streams, and in moist meadows watered by springs. Cultivated commercially as a salad vegetable.

DESCRIPTION Aquatic, hardy perennial with succulent, hollow, branching stems from 30–60cm(1–2ft). The creeping or floating stems root easily and bear fleshy, shiny, heart-shaped leaves. The leaves are very dark green to brownish green or bronze. From early summer to mid-autumn, clusters of small white flowers appear at the tips of the stems.

GROWING TIPS Watercress is easily propagated from cuttings left to root in water. It requires rich, very moist soil and frequent watering.

White Horehound

Marrubium vulgare

Labiatae

White horehound contains a bitter principle, marrubiin, and was one of the bitter herbs eaten by the Hebrews at the Passover. *Har hune* means hairy plant in Old English and is thought to be the origin of the plant's common name, horehound. Other authorities maintain that the name refers to Horus, the Egyptian sky god and son of Isis and Osiris. The herb was indeed known to the ancient Egyptians who employed it medicinally.

Today white horehound is valued for its expectorant properties and has long been one of the principal herbal remedies for chest complaints. Horehound tea and cough mixtures were popular from the beginning of the seventeenth century, and both Gerard and Culpeper thought highly of the herb. Gerard writes: 'a syrup made from the greene fresh leaves and sugar is a most singular remedie against the cough and wheezing of the lungs'. In rural England, horehound was widely grown for its medicinal properties and horehound candy was a favourite household remedy for coughs. Emigrants from England took the plant to North America and horehound cough preparations were popular with the Shakers. A hot infusion of the leaves also promotes sweating, and horehound tea sweetened with honey is a traditional remedy for feverish colds. This versatile herb also has a mild sedative action, and small amounts have been successful in regulating an over-rapid heartbeat.

At one time, white horehound was considered a cure for an impressive range of ailments from the bites of rabid dogs to tumours and failing eyesight. Taken cold, white horehound promotes the secretion of bile, aiding the whole digestive process, and it was for this tonic effect that horehound ale was traditionally brewed and drunk in the eastern region of England. Horehound was once added to stews, salads, and sauces, but its bitter menthol flavour is not to everyone's taste.

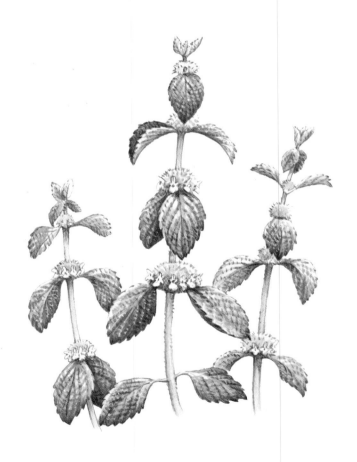

HABITAT Native to central and southern Europe, western Asia, and North Africa. Naturalized in the UK and North America. Found on field edges, waste ground, and rough pastureland, on dry, sandy or chalky soil.

DESCRIPTION Branching, bushy, perennial with erect, square stems from 60–90cm(2–3ft), and bearing some resemblance to catnip. The whole plant is covered in whitish hairs giving it a woolly appearance. The leaves are arranged in opposite pairs up the stem and are rounded to oval in shape with dentate margins. They are faintly aromatic, with downy, wrinkled upper surfaces. Whorls of numerous white, tubular flowers bloom towards the top of the stem throughout the summer.

Wild Carrot

Daucus carota

Umbelliferae

Queen Anne's Lace, bird's nest

The root of wild carrot is tough and unpleasant-tasting, but the leafy stems have an antiseptic and diuretic action. Carrot-leaf tea is a traditional remedy for bladder problems, while the seeds settle the stomach, easing flatulence.

HABITAT Native to Europe, North Africa, and western Asia. Found wild in hedgerows, pastureland and field edges, especially near the coast, on dry, sandy or chalky soil.

DESCRIPTION Biennial on a thin, white, very fibrous root. The furrowed, hairy stems grow from 60–90cm(2–3ft) and bear feathery, dark green leaves with sheathed bases. From mid-summer dense, flattened terminal umbels of creamy white flowers appear, each with a central deep purple flower. As the seeds ripen, the heads shrink and curve inwards to form a cup.

Wild Yam

Dioscorea villosa

Dioscoreaceae

Colic root

Wild yam is a traditional remedy for bilious colic and was once considered beneficial in morning sickness. The Mexican wild yam *Dioscorea mexicana* has proved particularly valuable medicinally: the root yields the essential hormonal component of the original female contraceptive pill, diosgenin.

HABITAT Native to North America from Rhode Island southwards to Florida. Vine that grows in thickets and hedges, and over fences.

DESCRIPTION Perennial vine with slender, tuberous, knotted rootstock and twining, woody stems that are reddish brown in colour and grow from 1.5–4.5m(5–15ft). The broad leaves are oval to heart-shaped and smooth in texture. Small yellowish-green flowers appear from early to mid-summer on drooping stems.

Willow
Salix alba spp.

Salicaceae
White willow

Willow bark has been used for centuries to reduce pain and inflammation, and to lower temperature in fevers. In the 1820s the active ingredient, salicin, was isolated and later formed the basis of the common drug aspirin. It was once traditional to wear the leaves following disappointment in love.

HABITAT Native to Europe and introduced into northern temperate zones, including North America. Found along the banks of rivers and streams, and in wet meadows, often near habitation. More common as an ornamental.

DESCRIPTION Tall, graceful tree to 20m(65ft) with greyish-brown, deeply fissured bark. The long, steeply angled branches are obscured by distinctive silvery blue-green, narrow, tapering leaves that curl at the tip. In spring drooping yellow, male catkins appear. The fruiting female catkins are initially green then become white and fluffy.

Wintergreen
Gaultheria procumbens

Ericaceae
Mountain tea

Native American Indians applied wintergreen to ease aching and arthritic limbs. The menthol-flavoured leaves were a tea substitute and an infusion was employed for sore throats. Wintergreen oil contains pain-relieving salicylates and makes a soothing rub for strained muscles and joints.

HABITAT Native to eastern North America from Canada southwards to Georgia. Grows in open woodland at the base of trees, and in clearings, providing ground cover.

DESCRIPTION Evergreen shrub with creeping, woody branches to 15cm(6in) that bear tufts of oval, shiny, bright green leaves. They are leathery in texture and have serrated margins. Nodding, bell-shaped white flowers appear in mid-summer followed by round, scarlet berries.

Witch Hazel

Hamamelis virginiana

Hamamelidaceae

Snapping hazelnut

Witch hazel's flexible, forked twigs have long been used for water divining purposes, and also to ascertain whether a person was guilty of murder or theft. The common name is derived from an Anglo-Saxon word, *wic-en*, meaning to bend, owing to the pliancy of the wood. Wicca, however, is also an old name for witchcraft, and a confusion of meaning led to the connection between witches and witch hazel. In Teutonic mythology the hazel was sacred to Thor, and the early Saxons frequently chose hazel groves as the sites of their temples. Woven hazel twigs were used in the construction of the earliest English Christian church at Glastonbury. Witch hunters, too, carried hazel twigs as protection from the evil eye, and Saint Patrick banished the snakes from Ireland with a hazel rod.

Witch hazel bark, twigs and leaves contain astringent tannins that reduce inflammation and stem bleeding. Native Americans first employed witch hazel poultices to ease swellings, and to soothe haemorrhoids and eye inflammations. Witch hazel tea was considered a general tonic, and also relieved mouth ulcers and inflamed throats. The medicinal properties of the tree soon came to the notice of early European settlers and witch hazel became a popular home remedy. It was listed as an official drug in the United States' Pharmacopeia in 1882 and is still recommended by modern herbalists to treat haemorrhoids, varicose veins, conjunctivitis, cuts, bruises and swellings. Today, distilled witch hazel is one of the most common first-aid remedies in household medicine cabinets. Its mild astringency has also made it a popular ingredient of skin cleansers and aftershaves.

HABITAT Native to North America except the far west. Found in damp, open woods and along stream banks from Nova Scotia eastwards to Minnesota and southwards to Georgia. Grown as an ornamental in parks and gardens and cultivated commercially.

DESCRIPTION Deciduous, spreading shrub or small tree from 2.5–4.6m(8–15ft) forking into several long, crooked branches that are covered in smooth greyish-brown bark. The leaves are elliptical to obovate in shape with unevenly scalloped edges and roughish undersides. They are downy when young and turn a luminous yellow in autumn. In early autumn, as the leaves fall, the tree bears clusters of bright yellow flowers with four, narrow strip-like petals and yellowish-brown interiors. These are followed by nut-like seeds capsules that do not ripen until the following autumn.

Woodruff

Asperula odorata or *Galium odoratum*

Rubiaceae

Sweet woodruff, *Waldmeister* (Ger)

Sweet woodruff's coumarin content is responsible for the fragrant, hay-like scent that develops when the flowering stems are dried. In Medieval times, woodruff was widely employed as a strewing herb, and its fresh, long-lasting perfume made it a popular mattress stuffing. In Germany, woodruff was used to flavour new wine and wine cups, a tradition dating from the thirteenth century. The wine, usually Rhine wine, is still drunk in some parts on the first of May to welcome the spring, and is known as the 'May drink' or 'May bowl'. Adding fresh woodruff, brandy and sugar, improves the taste and body of the tart young wine. Steep fresh woodruff in white wine for delicious summer wine cups or infuse it in brandy before making punch.

In the Middle Ages, woodruff was considered an important medicinal herb. The fresh leaves were applied to cuts and wounds, and a tea was drunk to ease stomach cramps. The herb was still valued medicinally in the sixteenth and seventeenth centuries when Gerard wrote of woodruff 'It is reported to be put into wine, to make man merry, and to be good for the heart and liver, it prevaileth in wounds . . .'. Today, the herb is rarely employed by medical herbalists and the US Food and Drug Administrtion consider it safe for use only in alcoholic drinks. In large quantities, it may cause vomiting and dizziness, and coumarin has caused liver damage in laboratory animals.

The herb's common name refers to its wooded habitat and the wheel-like arrangement of the leaves on the stem: 'ruff' is from the old French *rouelle* or wheel. On account of its fragrance, the French called the herb 'musk of the woods', while listed among its English country names are ladies-in-the-hay and sweet grass. In Germany woodruff is known as *waldmeister*, meaning master of the wood.

HABITAT Native to Europe, Asia and North Africa, and introduced elsewhere. Cultivated in the USA. Found wild in woods, especially beech woods, and shady banks and hedgerows on moist, loamy soil. Provides good ground cover.

DESCRIPTION Perennial with erect, smooth, slender stems to 25cm(10in) with whorls of six to nine leaves arranged at intervals along them, like the spokes of a wheel. The narrow leaves are dark green and lance-shaped with rough edges. From early summer small, white, tubular flowers bloom in loose clusters, followed by bristly seed balls, like cleavers. When fresh the plant is odourless.

Wormwood

Artemisia absinthium

Compositae
Absinthe

Wormwood has been used medicinally to expel intestinal worms for over 3500 years. *Absinthium*, the plant's specific name, denotes the traditional and most celebrated use of wormwood – in the potent French drink, absinthe, reputedly first prepared by witches. Wormwood is one of the most bitter herbs known and has a long history of use in medicinal alcoholic cordials. The plant, via the Old English *wermod* (spirit mother) and the German *wermut*, gives its name to vermouth, for which it is still used as a flavouring. Absinthe, on the other hand, has been banned from most countries due to the alarming effects of this habit-forming drink, including hallucinations and epileptic-like convulsions. Habitual use of commercial absinthe, said to be 68 per cent alcohol by volume, leads to irreparable damage to the nervous system, general paralysis, and death. Some sources ascribe Van Gogh's mental disturbances to an over-fondness for absinthe, while Degas' celebrated painting *The Absinthe Drinkers* displays the hopelessness of the absinthe addict.

Wormwood, in addition to its worm-expelling properties, is a bitter stomach remedy of long standing that helps to restore a poor appetite and eases a wide range of digestive problems. The herb also acquired a reputation as a liver and gall bladder tonic, which explains its popularity in alcoholic drinks for enfeebled livers. Externally, a compress of the leaves was applied to painful rehumatic joints, to stimulate poor circulation, and also to hasten childbirth and expel the afterbirth.

In the home, wormwood was a traditional insect repellant, and was strewn over floors and placed among clothes and linen. For its bitter taste, wormwood was used in brewing beer before the advent of hops. In some parts of eastern Europe a sprig may be added to a bottle of wine or vodka.

HABITAT Native to the Mediterranean and central Europe. Introduced to North America from Newfoundland south to Montana. Naturalized in temperate zones. Grows wild on roadsides and waste ground.

DESCRIPTION Shrubby, spreading, very aromatic perennial to 75cm(2½ft) with hairy stems and greyish, pinnate leaves that are deeply divided into narrow, blunt-ended segments. The leaves are dark green in colour and covered in silky, greyish hairs: the undersides are also downy. From mid-summer to mid-autumn, small, globular, greenish-yellow flowers appear on slender, erect stalks.

Woundwort

Stachys palustris

Labiatae

Marsh woundwort, clown's woundwort, all-heal

Woundwort is a close relative of betony, *Stachys officinalis*. Like betony, the plant enjoyed a considerable reputation as a healer from the Middle Ages onward, hence its common name, all-heal. Woundwort was principally employed for healing cuts and wounds, usually in the form of a poultice of the fresh leaves. Gerard actively promoted the herb in the latter part of the sixteenth century after visiting a farmer who had healed his own deep scythe wound with a poultice of bruised, fresh woundwort. When the celebrated herbalist offered to treat the wound himself free of charge and the farmer turned him down, Gerard christened the herb 'clown's woundwort'. Afterwards Gerard claimed to have 'cured many grievous wounds, and some mortale with the same herb'.

Woundwort has long been a traditional remedy for cramp, gout, and painful joints, due to its antispasmodic action, and modern herbalists continue to prescribe the herb for cramping pains. The herb also has astringent and antiseptic properties, hence its efficacy in staunching bleeding and healing wounds. In folk medicine direct application of the fresh leaves is still recommended for cuts and wounds, while a tea of the leaves is thought to be helpful for diarrhoea.

Country people once collected the large, tuberous roots of the herb and ate them boiled as a vegetable. Young woundwort shoots were also considered edible, despite their unpleasant smell, and cooked like asparagus.

Hedge woundwort, *Stachys sylvatica*, is a related species with branching stems, large nettle-like, coarsely toothed leaves, and dark, reddish-purple flowers. Like marsh woundwort, the bruised leaves have healing properties and were once employed in the treatment of wounds and swellings.

HABITAT Native to Europe and common in the UK in marshy meadows, and by rivers, streams and ditches. Widely distributed in northern temperate zones.

DESCRIPTION Nettle-like perennial with stout, quadrangular stems from 60–90cm(2–3ft) and long-stalked basal leaves that wither before flowering. The oblong, lance-shaped leaves have rounded bases that clasp the stem and taper to a narrow point. They are arranged in pairs up the stem, and both leaves and stem are hairy. From late summer spikes of mauve, two-lipped, mottled flowers bloom in whorls of six at the tip of the stem.

Yarrow

Achillea millefolium

Compositae

Milfoil, soldier's woundwort, carpenter's weed, nosebleed, devil's nettle

Yarrow has been highly valued for its medicinal properties since the earliest times, and pollen from the plant has been found in burial sites from the Neanderthal era. The ancient Chinese threw yarrow stalks when consulting the celebrated book of divination, the *I Ching*, also known as the *Yarrow Stalk Oracle*. The Greeks, too, employed yarrow medicinally during the Trojan wars. According to some authorities the herb was named *Achillea*, after the Greek hero Achilles who used it to staunch the wounds of his men on the battlefield. Others maintain the herb's healing properties were discovered by a herbalist named Achilles. The specific name *millefolium*, like the country name milfoil, refers to the many leaf segments, while the common name is thought to be a corruption of the Anglo-Saxon *gearwe* and the Dutch *yerw*.

The English country names, soldier's woundwort and carpenter's weed, are testimony to yarrow's great reputation as a wound healer. The astringency of the bruised leaves is helpful for stemming the flow of blood and the herb was still being used to treat soldiers' wounds during the American Civil War. The country name, nosebleed, is another indication of its usefulness for bleeding: the fresh leaves were simply pushed into the nostrils. Yarrow's healing properties were highly esteemed by several Native American Indian tribes, including the Blackfoot, who applied the herb to cuts, wounds, and bruises. They also considered the herb a spiritual aid and drank yarrow tea for a wide range of ailments from internal bleeding to fevers and sickness. Yarrow was also well known to the Shakers who employed it as a digestive and general tonic. In Native American and European folk medicine, yarrow has been employed to reduce swellings and to ease rheumatic joints, and modern research has confirmed that the herb possesses an anti-inflammatory action. Yarrow also promotes sweating and hot yarrow tea is a traditional home remedy of long standing for severe colds. Today, herbalists still consider yarrow one of the principal herbal remedies for fever, feverish colds and 'flu, often in combination with elderflower and peppermint.

As a cosmetic, yarrow makes an effective skin cleanser and toner on account of its astringency. Yarrow tea, made with the flowering stems, is said to be particularly beneficial for greasy skin.

HABITAT Native to Europe and naturalized in North America and temperate zones. Common in pastures, on embankments, roadsides and waste ground.

DESCRIPTION Perennial with an erect, rough, angular stem to 90cm(3ft) with attractive, feathery foliage. The very finely cut leaves clasp the stem towards the top, while the lower leaves are stalked. Both leaves and stem are covered in fine white hairs. Throughout the summer numerous, small daisy-like flowers bloom in flat-topped clusters. They are usually white in colour but may be tinged with pink.

Yellow Dock

Rumex crispus

Polygonaceae

Curled dock

Yellow dock, a traditional European and Native American remedy, is an effective inner cleanser. The root acts as a mild laxative that also stimulates the liver, and herbalists consider it helpful for eruptive skin problems. The fresh leaves relieve nettle stings.

HABITAT Native to Europe and naturalized in North America. Widely distributed in temperate zones. A common weed in fields and ditches, on roadsides and waste ground, in rich, heavy soils.

DESCRIPTION Perennial on stout, spindle-shaped taproot that is brown externally and yellowish inside. The slender stem from 30–90cm (1–3ft) bears oblong to lance-shaped light green leaves with wavy edges. The lower leaves may be over 30cm (1ft) in length. Throughout the summer small greenish or reddish flowers bloom in whorls along the upper stem.

Yellow Jessamine

Gelsemium sempervirens

Loganiaceae

Yellow jasmine root, Carolina jasmine

Yellow jessamine root has a sedative action. Herbalists once prescribed it for neuralgia and migraine, but it is now considered toxic in relatively small doses. Yellow jessamine is a homeopathic remedy for headaches, colds, and 'flu.

HABITAT Native to southern USA, Mexico and Guatemala. Found in damp woods and thickets from Virginia southwards to Texas and Florida. Cultivated as an ornamental.

DESCRIPTION Perennial, twining, evergreen vine with woody, purple-brown rhizomes and slender, woody stems to 6m(20ft). These attach themselves to trees, climbing from one to the other, and bear lance-shaped, glossy, dark green leaves. From early to late spring beautiful, sweet-smelling, funnel-shaped yellow flowers appear in clusters.

BOTANICAL GLOSSARY

Aerial part any part of a plant that grows above ground.

Annual a plant that completes its life cycle from seed to maturity and death in one growing season.

Axil the angle formed between the main stem and a branch, leaf stalk or flowering stem.

Biennial a plant that completes its life cycle from seed to maturity and death over two growing seasons. Flowering and fruiting often occur in the second year.

Deciduous a plant or tree that loses its leaves in autumn.

Floret a small flower, part of a head or cluster.

Herb a plant or part of a plant that is valued for its medicinal, culinary or aromatic properties.

Herbaceous a plant that is not woody and has leafy growth which dies down in winter.

Leaflet a segment of a compound leaf.

Lobe a rounded segment of a leaf.

Perennial a plant that lives for three or more growing seasons.

Rhizome an underground stem, usually growing horizontally, that bears shoots above and roots beneath.

Root a plant's main underground storage organ that anchors it in the ground.

Rootstock a short, thick rhizome, especially one that is not horizontal but more or less erect.

Runner a trailing stem that grows along the ground and produces roots.

Sepal a leaf-like part, usually green, that sheathes a flower before it opens.

Stamen the male, pollen-bearing part of a flower.

Taproot a long, fleshy storage root that grows vertically.

Tuber a swollen underground storage organ, growing from a stem or root.

Terminal growing at the top.

Umbel a flat-topped or umbrella-shaped flower cluster with all the flower stalks radiating from a common point.

Whorl a circular arrangement, at the same level on a stem, of three or more leaves or flowers.

MEDICAL GLOSSARY

Analgesic pain-relieving.

Astringent causing contraction of tissues and reducing secretions. A substance used to stop bleeding, mucous discharge, and fluid loss.

Carminative helps to expel, or reduces the formation of, excess gas in the intestines.

Cathartic laxative.

Demulcent viscous substance that is soothing to inflamed tissue.

Digestive aiding the digestive process.

Diuretic increasing the volume and flow of urine.

Emetic causing vomiting.

Emollient softening and soothing substance, used externally.

Expectorant expels mucous from the respiratory system.

Mucilage sticky substance occurring in many plants that relieves irritations and inflammation.

Pharmacopeia a catalogue of officially-recognized drugs.

Purgative promotes dramatic emptying of the bowels.

Tonic invigorating or strengthening.

INDEX

exhaustion 135, 176; system 32, 38, 77, 97, 103, 110, 130, 160, 174, 176
Nettle 12, 17, 127; tea 127
Neuralgia 20, 40, 95, 103, 156, 188
Nipples, sore 58
Nutmeg/Mace 16, 19, 128

O

Oak 129; tea 129
Oats 16, 130; poultice 130
Ocimum basilicum 35
Oenothera biennis 78
Oils 9, 12, 14–19 *passim; see also under individual headings*
Olea europeae 130
Olive 14, 130; oil 14–16 *passim*, 130
Opium 9, 107, 144
Orange 19, 131; oil 131
Oregano 10, 12, 14–16 *passim*, 115
Origanum marjorana 114; *vulgare* 115

P

Palpitations 121, 153, 175
Panax ginseng/pseudoginseng 9, 30; *quinquefolium* 91
Pansy, Wild 132
Papaver somniferum 9, 144
Paracelsus 8, 31
Parkinson's disease 38, 103
Parkinson, John 8, 119, 122, 123
Parsley 10, 13–17 *passim*, 87, 133; tea 133; Piert 132
Pasque Flower 134
Passiflora incarnata 135
Passionflower 135; tea 135
Peach 136; oil/poultice/tea 136
Pennyroyal 12, 19, 137; oil/tea 137
Pepper 16, 138; oil 138
Peppermint 118, 137; oil/tea 118
Perfume 16, 39, 69, 101, 131, 155, 169, 174, 175
Periwinkle 139; tea 139
Peruvian Bark 140
Pesticides, natural 12, 77, 147
Petroselinum crispum 133
Phytolacca americana 142
Picrasma excelsa 147
Piles 56, 83, 98, 139, 183
Pimenta dioica/officinalis 23
Pimpinella anisum 28
Pine 16, 141; kernels 15, 141; oil 18, 141
Pinus sylvestris 141
Piper nigrum 138
Plantago major 141
Plantain 141; poultice 141
Pleurisy 84; Root 142
Pliny 7, 32, 48, 116, 119, 143, 148
Poisons 9, 20, 38, 45, 46, 73, 85, 94, 95, 103, 108, 112, 120, 134, 142, 170, 172, 188; antidote 21, 88, 94, 129, 133, 152
Poke Root 142
Polish 84, 99
Polygonatum nultiflorum 162
Polygonum bistorta 41
Pomander 19, 65
Pomegranate 143
Poppy, White 9, 144; oil 144
Portulaca oleracea 146
Pot pourri 18–19, 59, 101, 131, 175
Potentilla reptans/canadensis 64
Pregnancy 9, 46, 137, 140, 149, 152, 164, 170, 172, 176, 177
Premenstrual syndrome 78
Preservatives 7, 63, 65, 125, 170, 173
Prickly Ash 145
Primula veris 70

Prostate problems 69, 99, 145, 158
Prunella vulgaris 159
Prunus amara 24; *amygdalus/dulcis* 24; *persica* 136
Psoriasis 51, 78, 83, 132, 157
Pulmonaria officinalis 111
Pumpkin 145
Punica granata 143
Purgatives 25, 101, 112, 142, 179
Purslane 146; tea 146
Pyrethrum 12, 19, 147

Q

Quassia 12, 147
Quassia amara 147
Quercus robur 129
Quince 148
Quinine/Quinidine 9, 140
Quinsy 43

R

Rabies 160
Ranunculus ficaria 56
Rash 25; poison-ivy 25, 37, 158
Raspberry 149; tea/vinegar 149
Repellants, disease 27; insect 19, 35, 75, 77, 82, 106, 137, 147, 170, 178, 185; moth 19, 31, 51, 65, 106, 122, 131, 164
Reproductive system, male 158; female 40, 58, 134
Restlessness 32, 58, 70, 107
Rhamnus purshiana 53
Rheumatism 33, 36, 44, 51, 56, 71, 74, 95, 98, 103, 104, 112, 115, 117, 118, 122, 127, 133, 142, 145, 152, 157, 163, 185–7 *passim*
Ribes nigrum 43
Romans 22, 28, 33, 60, 68, 72, 76, 80, 87, 93, 106, 118, 119, 124, 133, 136, 138, 139, 143, 144, 166, 168, 176, 178
Rosa canina 73
Rosemarinus officinalis 150
Rosemary 10–12, 14–19 *passim*, 150; oil 150
Rowan 151
Rubs 36, 50, 51, 110, 118, 182
Rubus fructicosus 42; *idaeus* 149; *strigosus* 149
Rue 12, 152
Rumex acetosa 163; *crispus* 188
Ruta graveolens 152

S

Saffron 153
Sage 10–12 *passim*, 15, 17, 19, 154; Clary 155; Red 155; tea 154
Salicylates/salicin 33, 117, 182
Salix alba 182
Salvia officinalis 154; *purpurea* 155; *sclarea* 155
Sambucus nigra 75
Sandalwood 157; oil 18, 157
Sanguinaria canadensis 45
Santalum album 157
Saponaria officinalis 162
Saponins 9, 162
Sarothamnus scoparius 49
Sarsaparilla 157
Sassafras 158; oil 158
Sassafras albidum 158
Satureia hortensis 166
Savory, Summer 12, 15, 166; Winter 10, 11, 166
Saw Palmetto 158
Scab 76
Scarlet fever 38
Sciatica 20, 95
Scrofula 83

Scrophularia nodosa 83
Scurvy 47, 146, 151, 163, 179
Scutellaria latifolia 160
Sedatives 32, 38, 40, 97, 103, 106, 107, 109, 112, 120, 122, 123, 139, 144, 161, 174
Self Heal 159
Senna 159
Serenoa serulata 158
Shock 29, 90
Silica 99, 127
Sinapis alba 125
Sinusitis 79, 141
Skin complaints 25, 46, 51, 64, 71, 78, 81, 83, 96, 121, 130, 170, 172, 178, 188; blisters 55, 106, 124 *see also individual headings*
Skullcap 160
Skunk Cabbage 161
Sleep aids 19, 54, 58, 95, 97, 105, 109, 128, 150, 169, 174
Slippery Elm 161
Smallpox 96
Smilax officinalis 157
Soapwort 17, 19, 162
Solidago virgaurea 92
Solomon's Seal 162; tea 162
Sorbus acuparia 151
Sores 61, 74, 81, 115, 136, 141, 143, 146, 158
Sorrel 14, 15, 146, 163
South Africa 50
Southernwood 19, 164
Spain 32, 39, 58, 87, 126, 131, 140, 153, 175
Sparteine 49
Spasms 38, 82, 103, 135
Spearmint 119; tea 119
Spirea ulmaria 117
Sprains 29, 67, 114, 152
Squaw Vine 164; tea 164
St John's Wort 156
Stachys officinalis 40; *palustris* 186; *sylvatica* 186
Stellaria media 61
Stings 30, 82, 116, 119, 141, 188
Stone Root 165
Storage 12–14, 16; drying 12–13, 16; freezing 13, 16
Strawberry, Wild 165; tea 165
Strewing 18, 59, 100, 105, 106, 115, 117, 119, 128, 162, 170, 184, 185
Sunburn 25
Sunflower 167; oil/poultice 167
Surgery 29, 90, 112
Sweating 32, 48, 54, 55, 75, 82, 89, 109, 137, 180, 187
Sweet Cicely 14, 15, 168; Violet 15, 17, 169
Swelling 50, 67, 83, 94, 183, 186, 187
Symphytum officinale 67
Symplocarpus foetidus 161
Syphilis 157, 158
Szygium aromaticum 65

T

Tanacetum parthenium 82; vulgare 170
Tannins 9, 49, 183
Tansy 19, 170; poultice 170
Taraxacum officinale 71
Tarragon 12–15 *passim*, 171; vinegar 171
Teas *see under individual headings*
Teeth 58, 165; ache 65, 95, 124, 145, 146, 171; extractions 29
Tension 59, 97, 106, 121, 130, 134, 155, 176

Throat, sore 26, 33, 34, 37–9 *passim*, 42, 43, 100, 107, 110, 115, 116, 129, 149, 151, 154, 155, 159, 163, 169, 173, 182, 183
Thrush 58
Thuja 172; oil 172
Thuja occidentalis 172
Thyme 10–15, 17–19 *passim*, 173; oil 173
Thymus vulgaris 173
Tilia europea 109
Tobacco 29, 54, 66, 103, 110, 135
Travel sickness 89
Trigonella foenum-graecum 81
Trillium erectum 40
Tropaeolum majus 126
Tuberculosis 99, 100, 123, 168, 179
Tumours 94, 120, 169, 180
Tussilago farfara 66
Typhoid 87, 106, 179

U

Ulcers 58, 94, 99, 102, 116; lung 67; mouth 26, 64, 82, 149, 155, 183; stomach 116, 161
Ulmus fulva 161
Urinary problems 22, 33, 36, 64, 92, 95, 104, 116, 165; gravel 41, 99, 132, 176
Urtica dioica/urens 127

V

Valerian 174
Valeriana officinalis 174
Veins 98; varicose 113, 183
Verbascum thapsus 123
Verbena, Lemon 11, 15, 16, 19, 175; oil/tea 175
Verbena officinalis 176
Veronica beccabunga 50
Veronicastrum virginicum 44
Vervain 16, 176
Vinca major 139
Vinegars 14
Viola odorata 169; *tricolor* 132
Virginia Snakeroot 177
Viscum album 120
Vomiting 39, 63, 65, 119, 149, 177, 184, 187

W

Walnut 18, 19, 178; oil 178
Warts 73, 136, 172
Watercress 15, 179
Weddings 93, 114, 131, 148, 150
White Horehound 180; tea 180
Whooping cough 38, 43, 87, 136
Wild Carrot 181; Yam 181
Willow 17, 182
Wintergreen 182; tea 182
Witch Hazel 17, 183; poultice/tea 183
Withering, William 85
Woodruff 18, 19, 117, 184; tea 184
Worms 34, 136, 145, 147, 170, 173; tape 70, 143
Wormwood 12, 19, 97, 185
Wounds 21, 30, 67, 74, 92, 99, 106, 113, 116, 136, 139, 141, 156, 159, 168, 176, 178, 184, 186, 187
Woundwort 186; poultice/tea 186

Y

Yarrow 11, 12, 17, 187; tea 187
Yellow Dock 188; Jasmine 188

Z

Zanthoxylum americanum 145
Zingiber officinale 89